Course	Organic Chemistry Laboratory CHM 375 & CHM 376
Course Number	**CHM 375 & CHM 376**
	University of Portland

http://create.mcgraw-hill.com

ISBN-10: 039081881X   ISBN-13: 9780390818812

Contents

Credits

Chapter 1

Techniques in the Organic Chemistry Laboratory

Basic laboratory operations used in the organic laboratory are introduced in this chapter. Mastery of these techniques will allow you to perform numerous organic experiments later in the course. Brief laboratory exercises are included as practical illustrations of each technique. Each exercise is designed to focus on a single technique. Until you have mastered the techniques, you may wish to use this chapter as a reference as you encounter each technique in different experiments throughout the course.

Technique A: Glassware and Equipment *Heating and Cooling*

Introduction

Checking out an equipment locker in the organic laboratory is like receiving presents during the holidays—everyone has lots of new toys to try out! Most of the items in the locker are made of glass and all are used in some way to perform reactions, work up reaction mixtures, or purify and analyze products.

Two types of glassware are used in the organic laboratory. **Microscale** glassware is stored in a case of about the same size as a laptop computer. Each item of glassware has its own individually shaped space, allowing for easy storage between use. Plastic screwcaps and liners are used as fast and efficient connectors or lids for the glassware.

A second type of glassware is **miniscale** glassware. The joints are ground-glass standard-taper joints that are made to fit snugly together. Miniscale glassware is often stored in a case, but if this glassware is stored loose in a drawer, it is important to arrange the items so that they don't bump into one another when the locker is opened.

Other useful items of glassware commonly found in the locker are thermometers, Erlenmeyer flasks, graduated cylinders, and beakers. Thermometers should always be stored in their plastic or cardboard containers. Beakers are best stored as nests. Graduated cylinders should be laid on their sides. If items are kept in the same place in the drawer after each lab period, it is easy to find the equipment you need.

Microscale Glassware and Related Equipment

Items commonly found in a threaded microscale glassware kit are shown in Figure 1A-1. A **Claisen adapter** (a) is a special piece of glassware that allows for placement of more than one item on top of a reaction vessel. A **distillation head** (b) is for distillation

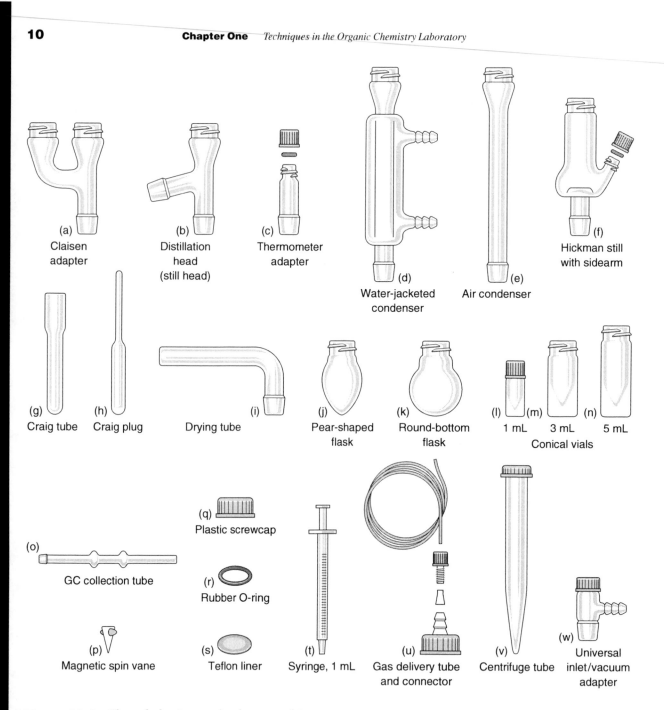

Figure 1A-1   Threaded microscale glassware kit

of 5 mL or more of a liquid. (Not all kits are equipped with this piece.) A **thermometer adapter** (c) is included so that a thermometer may be mounted on top of the distillation head. A **water-jacketed condenser** (d) allows cold water to flow around the outer compartment of the condenser. This condenser is used when volatile reagents and solvents are used during a reaction. It can also be used as an air condenser.

An **air condenser** (e) has no outer compartment. It may be packed and used as a fractional distilling column or it may be placed on top of a vial to heat high-boiling liquids. The **Hickman still** (f) consists of a tube, similar to the air condenser, but with a circular lip to trap liquid during a micro-distillation. The Hickman still may have a side arm (as shown here) for easy removal of condensed liquid. The **Craig tube and plug** (g, h) are used for isolating small quantities of crystals. In some kits, both pieces are made of glass. Great care must be taken so as not to break either of the parts during use. The bent tube is a **drying tube** (i), which is designed to fit on top of a condenser. The tube is packed with fresh drying agent prior to use.

Some kits contain a 10-mL **pear-shaped flask** (j), used for distillations. A 10-mL **round-bottom flask** (k) is used for distillation or for carrying out reactions that require no more than 5–8 mL total volume of solution. A magnetic stir bar (not shown) is sometimes used with the round-bottom flask. The **conical vials** (l,m,n) are the most used items of equipment in the kit. The vials have capacities of 1, 3, and 5 mL. The **gas-liquid chromatography (GC) collection tube** (o) is used for collecting condensed liquid samples at the exit ports of the gas chromatography instrument. A **magnetic spin vane** (p) is designed for use with the conical vials. Each conical vial is equipped with a **plastic screwcap** (q). The screwcaps have openings that allow insertion of other items, such as condensers. Each conical vial is equipped with a **rubber O-ring** (r). Round **Teflon liners** (s) may be placed inside the plastic screwcap to close off vials from the outside atmosphere. The Teflon liner may be penetrated with a syringe needle when adding a solution to a vial via syringe while the system is closed.

The kit should also contain a 1-mL **syringe** (t). The syringe may be made of glass with a Teflon plunger. This glass syringe is reusable and should be cleaned between usage. Some kits contain disposable syringes made of plastic. Needles are generally not included in the kits. They will be distributed when needed. Most kits contain a **gas delivery tube** assembly (u) that includes four parts. The tube is used to transport any gas formed during a reaction to a separate container. A **centrifuge tube** (v) can be used with both the Craig tube and the glass tubing. The kit also includes a **universal inlet/vacuum adapter** (w).

Some kits may vary in content; it is not necessary to have all of the items in each kit. Other glassware used in microscale experiments is shown in Figure 1A-2, including a **Hirsch funnel** (a) containing a porous plug, to be used with a **suction flask** (b) to collect solid products by filtration, a separate **filter adapter** (c), a microscale **chromatography column** (d), a **pipet** (e), and a **spatula** (f).

Microscale experiments can also be done using test tubes, small Erlenmeyer flasks, Pasteur pipets, small beakers, and other glassware.

Miniscale Glassware

Using stardard-taper glassware may be new to you. If this glassware is furnished in your locker in the form of a kit, it will look similar to the kit shown in Figure 1A-3. The kit consists of some items of glassware that have standard-taper joints. The joint sizes may be 14/20 or 19/22. The designation 14/20 means that the inside width is 14 mm and the joint is 20 mm long. Glassware with 14/20 and 19/22 joints is known as miniscale. A similar but larger form of this glassware has 24/40 joints and is called macroscale glassware. A dozen or more items make up the typical miniscale kit (see Figure 1A-3).

A **bleed tube** (a) is used for vacuum distillations. A **Claisen adapter** (b) allows for placement of more than one item on top of a reaction vessel. The **distilling head** (c) holds a thermometer and passes distillate into a condenser. A **thermometer adapter** (d) fits in the distilling head to hold a thermometer. A **bent vacuum adapter** (e) connects the condenser to the receiver in distillation. A **condenser** (f) is required to condense vapors during distillation. A **distillation column** (g) is used for reflux and also as a second condenser. Several **round-bottom flasks** (h–l) of various sizes are included. Extractions are accomplished by using a **separatory funnel** (m). A **stopper** (n) is necessary for the top of the separatory funnel.

Figure 1A-2

Additional glassware
for microscale
experiments

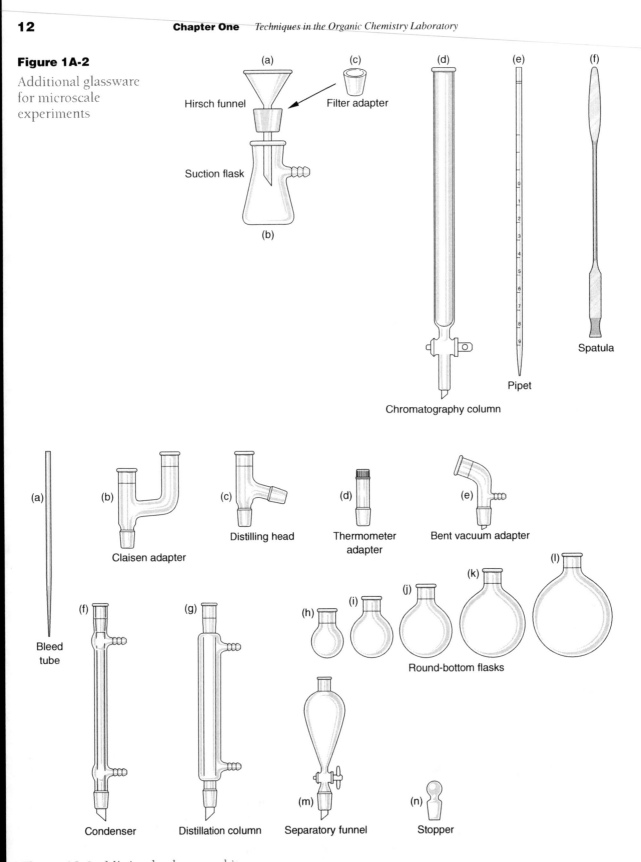

Figure 1A-3   Miniscale glassware kit

Additional Glassware and Equipment

Common glassware items, such as beakers, funnels, and Erlenmeyer flasks, are also generally stocked in student lockers. These and other items commonly found in student lockers are illustrated in Figures 1A-4 and 1A-5.

How to Clean Glassware

Dispose of all chemical residues properly and then wash glassware with soap and water. Use small amounts of acetone to clean organic residues that are difficult to remove. Use petroleum ether or a similar nonpolar solvent to remove grease from joints. Use a brush, if necessary, to scrub away charred matter. Treat flasks that are very resistant to cleaning with 3 M or 6 M nitric acid. **Clean all glassware immediately after use. Never put dirty glassware away in the locker.**

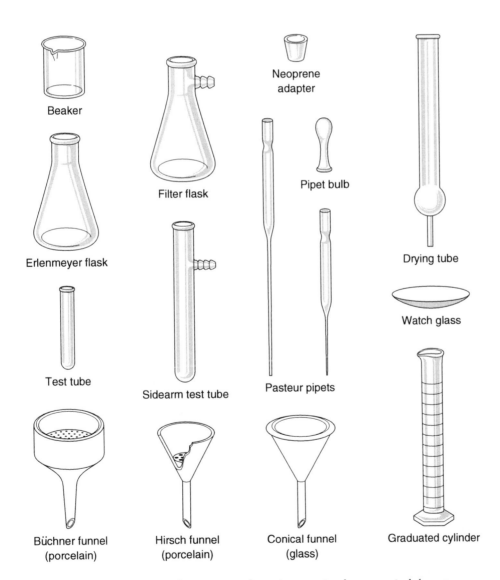

Figure 1A-4   Common glassware and equipment in the organic laboratory

Figure 1A-5

Common glassware
and equipment in the
organic laboratory

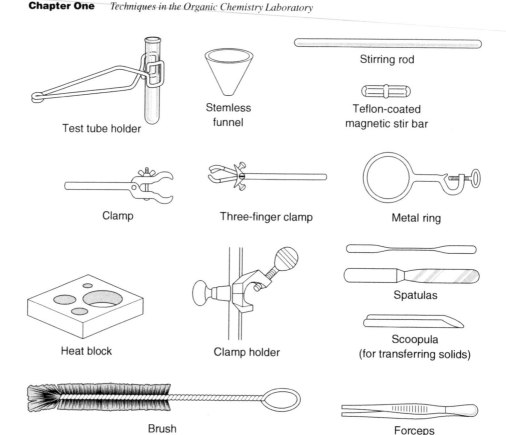

Test tube holder

Stemless funnel

Stirring rod

Teflon-coated magnetic stir bar

Clamp

Three-finger clamp

Metal ring

Heat block

Clamp holder

Spatulas

Scoopula (for transferring solids)

Brush

Forceps

How to Heat and Cool Glass Reaction Vessels

There are three methods for heating glassware in the laboratory.

Refer to Figures 1A-6 and 1A-7.

1. Use a **water bath** or **steam bath** to heat an Erlenmeyer flask or beaker by placing the item on or just above the bath. **Add a boiling chip, spin vane, or spin bar** and heat contents of the containers to any temperature as necessary up to just under the boiling point of water. Use a **hot plate** to heat a water bath and a steam line to heat a steam bath.

The temperature of sand in a sand bath is hard to control. Use a minimal amount of sand.

2. Use a **heat block** or a **sand bath** to heat vials in microscale experiments. **Add a boiling chip, spin vane, or spin bar** and place vials containing solutions in a metal heat block or in a sand bath (a glass crystallizing dish or metal container containing sand, for example) with a hot plate underneath as the heat source. Heat the sand bath 20–30°C above the boiling point of the solvent being evaporated or distilled because heat transfer through sand is not very efficient. **Be very careful when touching items near or on a hot plate.** It is hard to know if a heat block or sand bath is hot or cold.

Do not plug a heating mantle directly into an electrical outlet.

3. Use a variable **transformer (Variac)** and a **heating mantle** of the proper size to heat miniscale round-bottom flasks. Variacs and heating mantles may be new to you. To assemble, set the on/off switch to "off" and set the dial to a reading of zero. Insert the plug of the power cord of the Variac into a standard electrical outlet. Connect the second cord from the Variac to the heating mantle. Connect the heating mantle to the cord and use a clockwise rotation to lock the connection. Unlock only by a counter-clockwise rotation. Remember to "twist on" and "twist off" to connect or disconnect the cord to a heating mantle. **Add a boiling chip or spin bar** to the

flask being heated. Then add the chemicals to the flask. Turn on and adjust the Variac from 0 to 110 volts. The desired setting depends upon the volatility of the solvent being heated. For example, a setting of 20 volts will cause diethyl ether to boil, but a much higher setting of 70–80 volts must be used to boil water.

Common heating devices are shown in Figure 1A-6. They include a steam bath/hot water bath, a hot plate/stirrer with heat block, and a Variac transformer and heating mantle. An alternate to a fiberglass heating mantle is a Thermowell (Laboratory Craftsmen) heater. The Thermowell looks much like a fiberglass heating mantle, but is made of hard ceramic material. The Thermowell offers the advantage of not requiring an exact fit between the size of flask and well. A larger Thermowell will accommodate smaller-sized flasks. Use boiling chips or magnetic stirrer when heating liquids to boiling using a Thermowell heater.

Examples of setups for heating are shown in Figure 1A-7. These include a heat block, a sand bath, and a heating mantle. A steam bath can also be used as a hot water bath.

Glassware apparatus may also require cooling to moderate an exothermic reaction or when trying to obtain crystalline products. Ice baths are generally very effective for cooling. To make an ice bath, simply add ice to a beaker or water bath and partially submerge the vessel to be cooled. Add a stir bar or spin vane to the vessel to perform a reaction at cold temperatures with stirring.

Add sodium chloride or calcium chloride to an ice bath to make an ice-salt bath for those situations where temperatures from 0 to –10°C are required. To obtain even lower temperatures, place small chunks of dry ice in a dry metal or glass container to prepare special baths at –78°C. Carefully pour isopropyl alcohol or acetone over the dry ice. White carbon dioxide vapors will form during this process and some frothing may occur. Partially submerge the reaction flask to be cooled in the dry ice bath.

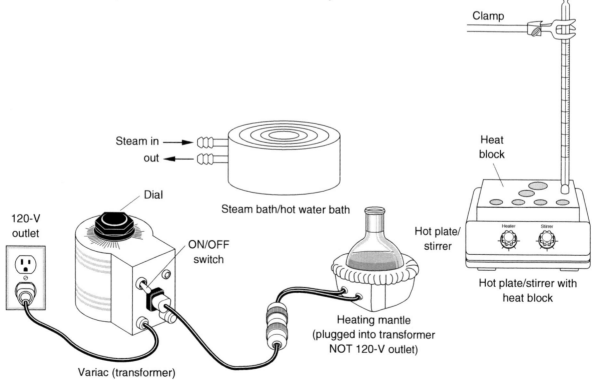

Figure 1A-6 Heating devices and accessories

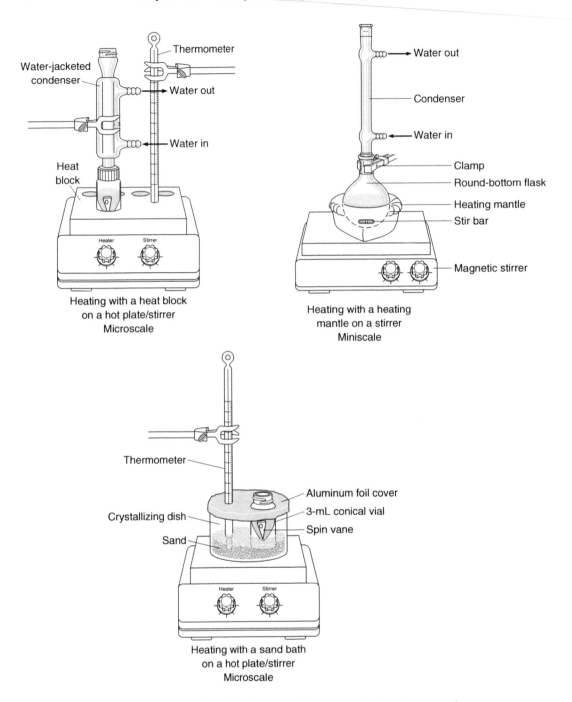

Figure 1A-7   Heating setups using a heat block, a sand bath, and a heating mantle

Questions

1. What types of reaction vessels are used in microscale experiments? Are these vessels different in any way from miniscale equipment?

2. An organic solvent has a boiling point of 120°C. What heating device should be used to remove the solvent?

3. Give a reason for not having a graduated cylinder included with microscale glassware.

Technique B: Weighing and Measuring

Introduction to Weighing

Because of the small quantities used in microscale experiments, solid and liquid reagents are usually weighed to three-place accuracy using a three-place or four-place, top-loading balance. For miniscale experiments, a two-place balance is often sufficient.

How to Weigh Solids and Liquids

Weigh solids into glass containers or onto weighing paper using a spatula. Weigh liquids in containers that can be capped. Transfer liquids with a Pasteur pipet. Place the container or paper on the balance pan of a top-loading balance and push the tare button. The scale of a three-place balance should read 0.000 g. Add the desired amount of substance in portions up to the desired weight. Record the actual amount used in your notebook. Use an amount that is within 1–2% of the weight given in each experiment. If too much sample is weighed out, transfer any excess material to an appropriate bottle provided by the instructor. **Clean the balance and the area around the balance when you have finished weighing.** A three-place, top-loading balance is shown in Figure 1B-1.

Do not weigh hot or warm objects.

Introduction to Measuring Volumes of Liquids

Volatile liquids should be measured with a calibrated glass pipet or syringe (by volume instead of weight) to avoid loss of liquid through evaporation. Three different kinds of pipets are available: a calibrated Pasteur pipet, a calibrated glass pipet (see Figure 1B-2), and an automatic delivery pipet (see Figure 1B-4). Use the calibrated Pasteur pipet for transfer of liquids where the exact amount of liquid isn't important. The pipet consists of two parts: a glass tube drawn to a blunt tip and a latex bulb. The glass tube is disposable, although it can generally be used a number of times. The bulb is used to draw liquid into the glass tube. Calibrated glass pipets are designed to measure liquids in increments of 0.01 mL to 50 mL. The 0.1-mL, 0.5-mL, and 1.0-mL pipets will be most useful in this course.

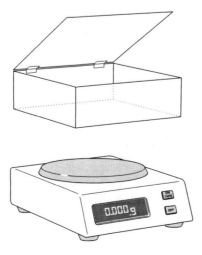

Figure 1B-1

A three-place, top-loading balance with draft shield

Figure 1B-2

Calibrated Pasteur pipet and calibrated glass pipet

Calibrated Pasteur pipet and bulb

Calibrated glass pipet

Figure 1B-3

Steps for filling and dispensing 0.50 mL of a liquid using a calibrated pipet

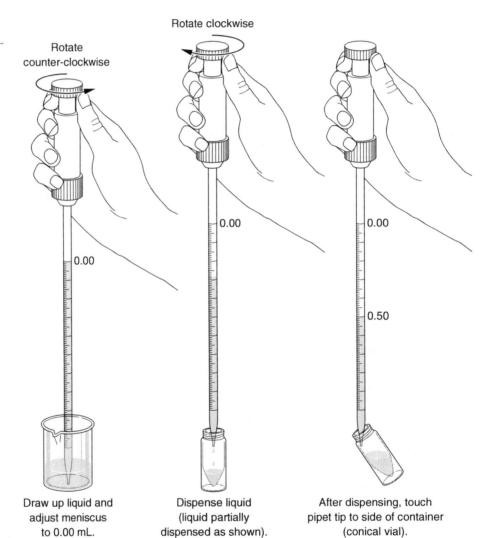

How to Use a Calibrated Glass Pipet

Do not pipet by mouth!

Use a pipet with either a bulb or a pipet pump. If you are using a pipet bulb, attach the bulb to the wide end of the pipet. Squeeze the pipet bulb. Place the tip of the pipet below the surface of liquid. Gently release pressure on the bulb allowing liquid to be drawn up into the pipet slightly above the 0-mL mark. Adjust the volume of liquid so that the meniscus of the liquid reads 0.00 mL. Place the tip of the pipet into the top of the receiving vessel and apply pressure to the bulb to dispense the liquid. Deliver the last drop of the desired volume by touching the tip against the wall of the vessel.

If dispensing using a pipet pump, see the steps shown in Figure 1B-3. Attach the pump to the wide end of the pipet. Place the tip of the pipet below the surface of liquid. Turn the knob at the top of the pump counter-clockwise to draw liquid into the pipet slightly above the 0-mL mark. Adjust the volume of liquid so that the meniscus of the liquid reads 0.00 mL. Place the tip of the pipet into the top of the receiving vessel and turn the pump knob clockwise to dispense 0.50 mL of the liquid. Deliver the last drop of the desired volume by touching the tip against the wall of the vessel.

If this procedure is difficult, which is often the case if the solvent is diethyl ether or a similar highly volatile solvent, it will be necessary to draw up the solvent a few times before dispensing. Transfer a slight excess of the amount of the solvent you want to pipet to a clean Erlenmeyer flask. Using a clean, dry pipet and filter bulb, draw up a portion of solvent and release to allow it to return to the flask. Repeat this process several times to equilibrate the temperature of the pipet and solvent. Then draw the solvent up to the mark on the pipet for delivery.

How to Use an Automatic Delivery Pipet

An automatic delivery pipet, illustrated in Figure 1B-4, is a device that can be set to deliver an exact volume of liquid (usually aqueous) by dialing in the desired volume at the top of the pipet. Pipets are available for different volumes and most pipets are adjustable to allow delivery of different volumes. The pipets are very expensive, so be careful when using them. Delivering volatile liquids may lead to inaccuracies.

The automatic delivery pipet consists of two parts, the main body and a disposable plastic tip. The tip is the only part of the pipet that touches the surface of the liquid. Liquid should never touch the main body of the pipet and even the tip should reach only just below the surface of the liquid being transferred. Differences in surface tension of organic liquids may affect the amount of a liquid drawn up at a particular pipet setting, so automatic delivery pipets are used most often to measure out aqueous solutions.

The steps for dispensing a liquid using an automatic delivery pipet are shown in Figure 1B-5. Attach a plastic tip to the bottom of the pipet and dial in the desired volume at the top of the pipet and lock in the values. Depress the piston to the first stop (first point of resistance). Do this before dipping the tip of the pipet below the surface of the liquid being dispensed. Next, insert the plastic tip 1–2 cm below the surface of the liquid and slowly release the plunger to load the pipet. This procedure prevents formation of bubbles. To dispense the liquid to a new container, touch the tip of the pipet against the container and depress the piston slowly to the first stop. Then push the piston to the second stop (all the way) to dispense the last drop of liquid. The same tip can be used again to dispense another sample of the same liquid. Replace the plastic tip to dispense a different liquid.

Figure 1B-4

The automatic delivery pipet (used mainly for dispensing aqueous solutions)

How to Use a Syringe

Use a syringe when a liquid must be injected with a needle. Clean and dry all parts of the syringe. Transfer a portion of liquid from the stock bottle to a vial. With the plunger inserted all the way into the barrel of the syringe, introduce the tip of the needle below the surface of the liquid in the vial. Carefully pull back on the plunger so that liquid is drawn up into the barrel to the desired volume. Drain the syringe into another container or inject the liquid through a septum into another vial. Remember that a dirty needle will contaminate the liquid.

To add a liquid to a reaction mixture for a reaction that must be run under a dry or inert atmosphere, push the needle of a loaded syringe through the cap liner or septum.

Figure 1B-5

Steps for dispensing a liquid using an automatic delivery pipet

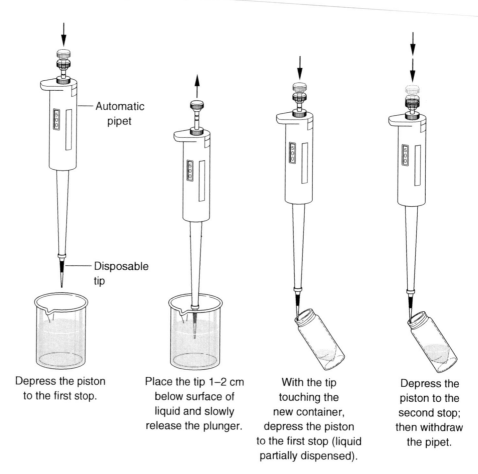

Automatic pipet

Disposable tip

| Depress the piston to the first stop. | Place the tip 1–2 cm below surface of liquid and slowly release the plunger. | With the tip touching the new container, depress the piston to the first stop (liquid partially dispensed). | Depress the piston to the second stop; then withdraw the pipet. |

Add the liquid in the syringe at a convenient rate by applying pressure to the plunger. Be careful when pushing a needle through a septum. The septum will offer some resistance, but most needles are sharp enough to penetrate a septum if a slow, steady pressure is applied. Obtain a new needle if excessive pressure is required.

Clean the syringe by drawing up a wash solvent (such as alcohol or acetone) and expelling the solvent into a suitable container. Do this several times. Set the syringe and plunger aside to dry. The needle should be detached and dried in an oven (placed in a beaker) if it is to be reused in the same lab period.

Be very careful when working with syringes. It is not uncommon to "get poked" by a needle. Be careful when placing a syringe on the lab bench. Syringes can roll off the bench easily and be damaged. They are expensive to replace. Disposable syringes are used in many laboratories. These syringes need not be cleaned, but must be properly discarded.

Safety First!

Always wear eye protection in the laboratory.

Exercise B.1: Determining Density of an Aqueous Solution

The balance pan should be clean and dry. Turn on and tare the balance. Place an empty capped 3-mL or 5-mL conical vial on the pan and record the weight. Attach a plastic tip to an automatic delivery pipet. Be sure that the setting at the top of the pipet corresponds to the desired volume of 0.500 mL. With the pipet held upright, push down on the piston to the first stop position. Place the tip of the pipet just below the surface of the stock bottle of an aqueous solution assigned by your instructor. Release the piston gradually to draw the liquid into the tip. Transfer the liquid from the pipet to the vial. Record the weight. Transfer the sample in the vial to a bottle labeled "recovered aqueous solutions" using a Pasteur pipet. Clean up any spilled liquid before leaving the balance area. Calculate the density of the solution.

Exercise B.2: Determining Density of an Organic Liquid

The balance pan should be clean and dry. Turn on and tare the balance. Place an empty capped 3-mL or 5-mL vial on the pan and record the weight. Use a calibrated or volumetric pipet and bulb or pipet pump to draw up 0.500 mL of an organic liquid from a sample of organic liquid issued by your instructor. Do this by initially drawing up more than 0.500 mL and then releasing a small amount back into the reservoir so that the meniscus reads 0.500 mL. Transfer the liquid from the pipet to the vial. Record the weight. Transfer the sample in the vial to a bottle labeled "recovered organic liquids" using a Pasteur pipet. Clean up any spilled liquid before leaving the balance area. Calculate the density of the liquid. Use Table 1B-1 to determine the identity of the liquid.

Safety First!

Always wear eye protection in the laboratory.

Exercise B.3: Calibrating a Pasteur Pipet

Calibrate a Pasteur pipet using a file or a marking pencil, at heights of liquid equal to 0.5, 1.0, 1.5, and 2.0 mL or other volumes if desired. Use a 1-mL syringe or a calibrated pipet to furnish the amounts of liquid to be measured. Mark three Pasteur pipets in case one gets broken. Insert a plug of cotton into one the pipets to make a "filter pipet." Filter pipets are used to trap solids during transfers from the pipet and to keep volatile, low-boiling solvents from being involuntarily released from the pipet. The calibrated Pasteur pipets will be used in future experiments.

Safety First!

Always wear eye protection in the laboratory.

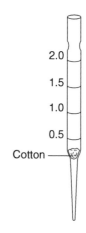

Questions

1. A microscale procedure requires 2.5 mL of diethyl ether. Describe the best method to measure this amount.

2. Describe the procedure for measuring out:

   a. 50 mg of an organic solid for a reaction to be run using a 3-mL vial.

   b. 1.00 mL of an organic liquid.

   c. approximately 0.5 mL of water.

3. Contrast and compare the capabilities and use of an automatic delivery pipet versus a syringe.

4. Why are liquids not poured from one container into another in microscale experiments?

5. Why might it be preferable to use a syringe rather than a pipet?

Table 1B-1 Densities of Selected Organic Liquids

Organic Compound	Density$^{20/4}$(g/mL)
Hexane	0.6603
3-Methylpentane	0.6645
Heptane	0.6837
Cyclohexane	0.7785
1-Propanol	0.8035
3-Pentanone	0.8138
p-Xylene	0.8611
Toluene	0.8669
Tetrahydrofuran	0.8892
Ethyl acetate	0.9003

Technique C: Melting Points

Introduction

Most organic compounds are molecular substances that have melting points below 300°C. The melting point of a solid compound is a physical property that can be measured as a method of identification. Melting points of pure compounds are recorded in handbooks of physical data, such as the *Handbook of Chemistry and Physics* (CRC). The reported melting point is that temperature at which solid and liquid phases exist in equilibrium. A melting point of a solid is actually a melting range, which starts from the temperature at which the first drop of liquid appears and ends at the temperature at which the entire sample is liquid. Students should report melting points as melting ranges. Sometimes only a single temperature is reported in the tables of physical properties; in this case, the value represents the upper temperature of the melting range.

The measured melting range gives a rough indication of the purity of the compound: the purer the compound, the higher its melting point and the narrower its melting range. Melting a solid requires energy to overcome the crystal lattice energy. Impurities disrupt the crystal lattice, so less energy is required to break intermolecular attractions; impurities thus generally lower and broaden the melting point. Since the decrease in melting point of a solid is generally proportional to the amount of impurity present, the difference between the expected melting point of the pure compound and the experimentally measured melting point gives a rough approximation of purity.

Figure 1C-1 is a phase diagram of a mixture of phenol and diphenylamine. The phase diagram is a graph of temperature versus composition. The top convex line represents the temperature at which the entire solid is melted, and the bottom concave line represents the temperature at which the solid just begins to melt. The distance between these two lines represents the melting point range. Pure phenol (at 0 mol percent diphenylamine) exhibits a sharp melting point at 41°C; that is, both the liquid and the solid line converge at 41°C. A sample of phenol containing 5 mol percent of diphenylamine begins to melt at 35°C and the solid is all melted by 40°C, giving a melting point range of 35–40°C. A sample of phenol containing 10 mol percent of diphenylamine has a melting point range of 30–37°C. As the amount of impurities increases, the melting point range becomes proportionally lower and broader.

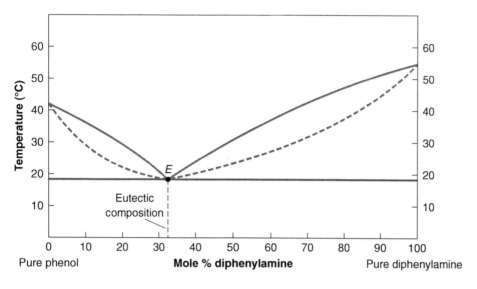

Figure 1C-1

Temperature vs. composition diagram of a phenol/diphenylamine binary mixture

It would be tempting to say that addition of impurities always lowers the melting point and broadens the melting point range. However, this is not the case. The lowest melting point on the phase diagram occurs at 32 mol percent diphenylamine. A sample of phenol containing this amount of diphenylamine melts sharply at 19°C. For a binary (two-phase system), the minimum melting point temperature is called the eutectic point, and the composition at this temperature is called the eutectic mixture. For the phenol/diphenylamine system, the eutectic point occurs at 32 mol percent diphenylamine. A mixture of 68 mol percent phenol and 32 mol percent diphenylamine (the eutectic composition) behaves like a pure compound, exhibiting a sharp melting point. Addition of more diphenylamine beyond the eutectic composition actually increases the melting point: a sample of phenol containing 40 mol percent diphenylamine begins to melt around 21°C.

Not all two-phase mixtures exhibit eutectic behavior; a sharp melting point is usually indicative of purity. However, a sharp melting point may also be obtained if the compound and impurity form a eutectic mixture. For nearly pure compounds, the presence of small amounts of impurities generally lowers the melting point. Purification generally affords crystals having a higher and sharper melting point than the impure solid. In rare cases, the melting point may rise when a certain additive is present.

Mixed Melting Behavior

Because impurities change (usually lower) the melting point, a mixed melting point can be used to determine whether two compounds are identical or different. Suppose that there are two beakers of a white solid sitting on the bench top. The melting point of each solid is found to be 133°C. Are the two solids the same or are they different? In a mixed melting point, samples of the two compounds are thoroughly mixed and a new melting point is measured. If the two compounds are not identical, the melting point of the mixture generally will be depressed and broadened. If the melting point is unchanged, the two compounds are most probably identical.

Melting Behavior of Solids

Several physical changes occur as a solid melts. In many cases, the crystals will soften and shrink immediately before melting. The crystals may appear to "sweat" as traces of solvent or air bubbles are released. These are normal occurrences, but shouldn't be considered as "melting." The melting point is measured beginning at the time the first free liquid is seen. Sometimes compounds decompose rather than melt. Decomposition usually involves changes such as darkening or gas evolution. Decomposition may occur at or even below the melting point for compounds that are thermally labile. In general, decomposition occurs over a fairly broad temperature range. For this reason, a sample should not be used in two consecutive melting point determinations. The sample may decompose, causing the second measured melting point to be lower than the first.

Some compounds having fairly high vapor pressures can change directly from a solid to a gas without passing through the liquid phase. This is called sublimation. In order to measure a melting point (more accurately, a sublimation point) for such compounds, a sealed, evacuated melting point capillary tube must be used.

Calibration of the Thermometer

Frequently, thermometers are not equally accurate at all temperatures and must be calibrated to obtain accurate melting points. To calibrate a thermometer, the melting points of pure solid samples are measured and a graph is made of the measured (observed) melting point temperatures versus the difference between the observed and the expected melting points. When reporting experimental melting points, corrections should be made by adding the appropriate value from the graph to the observed melting point. A sample thermometer calibration curve is shown in Figure 1C-2. An observed melting point of 190°C would be reported as 188°C (observed temperature + correction factor = 190°C + [–2°C] = 188°C).

Apparatus for Measuring Melting Points

Several commercial devices that measure melting points are available. These include the Mel-Temp apparatus and the Fisher-Johns Block, which are heated metal block devices. The Mel-Temp uses a closed-end capillary tube. The Fisher-Johns uses two glass plates horizontally placed to sandwich the substance between them. The Thomas-Hoover device is a mechanically stirred oil bath that also uses capillary tubes. These devices are shown in Figure 1C-3.

How to Determine a Melting Point

Preparing the sample. Use 1–2 mg of dry solid. For a mixed melting point determination, thoroughly mix approximately equal amounts of the two samples using a mortar and pestle.

Figure 1C-2

Temperature
calibration curve

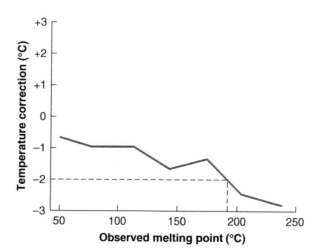

Figure 1C-3

Devices for measuring
melting points

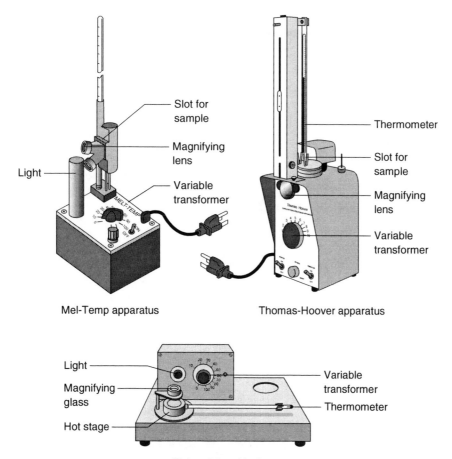

Mel-Temp apparatus   Thomas-Hoover apparatus

Fisher-Johns block

Loading the capillary. Do not load the capillary tube with too much sample: this causes the melting point to be wide and slightly high because the temperature will continue to rise while the compound continues to melt. Place 1–2 mg of the sample on a watch glass or a piece of weighing paper. Push the open end of the capillary down onto the sample and tap on the solid sample. Then invert the tube. Gently tap the bottom of the tube on the bench or drop the tube through a short 2-ft piece of glass tubing; this causes the sample to pack more tightly and give a more accurate melting point. This process is illustrated in Figure 1C-4.

Setting the heating rate. If the melting point is unknown, heat the sample rapidly to establish an approximate melting point. Turn off the apparatus as soon as the compound melts and note the temperature. Let the temperature drop until it is approximately 10°C below the observed melting point and repeat the melting point determination with a new sample. Heat the sample rapidly to within 10°C of the known melting point. Then slow to 1–2°C per minute. Heating too rapidly results in inaccurate, usually wider, melting point measurements. An appropriate heating rate can also be determined by referring to the heating-rate curve that often accompanies the melting point apparatus.

Observe the sample through the magnifying eyepiece as the sample melts. Record the melting point as the temperature from the start of melting until all solid is converted to liquid. Remember that shrinking, sagging, color change, texture changes, and sweating are not melting. When the sample has melted, turn off the melting point apparatus and remove the capillary tube. Discard the capillary after use into the glass disposal container.

Figure 1C-4

Loading a sample into a melting point capillary tube

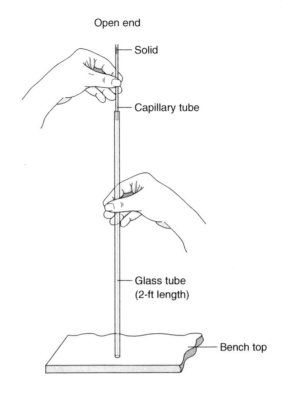

Open end

— Solid

— Capillary tube

— Glass tube
(2-ft length)

— Bench top

Exercise C.1: Calibration of a Thermometer

Safety First!

Always wear eye protection in the laboratory.

Determine the melting points of a series of pure solids. Suggested compounds are diphenylamine (53°C), *m*-dinitrobenzene (90°C), benzoic acid (122°C), salicyclic acid (159°C), succinic acid (189°C), and 3,5-dinitrobenzoic acid (205°C). Calculate the difference between the known melting point and the measured melting point for each compound. The differences will be positive or negative. Plot the measured melting point on the *x* axis and the correction factor on the *y* axis as in Figure 1C-2.

Exercise C.2: Melting Point of an Unknown Solid

Safety First!

Always wear eye protection in the laboratory.

Melting points should be recorded as corrected or uncorrected.

Calibrate the thermometer, if directed to do so by the instructor (Exercise C.1). Obtain a sample of an unknown solid and record the number of the unknown in your lab notebook. Load a capillary tube with a small amount of the solid. Prepare another sample in the same manner. Place the tube in a melting point apparatus. Heat rapidly to get an estimate of the actual melting point. Turn off the apparatus immediately when the compound melts and note the temperature. Let the temperature drop until it is approximately 10°C below the observed melting point. Then place the second tube in the melting point apparatus and start heating at a rate of 1–2°C per minute. Record the melting point range of the sample (corrected, if necessary). The unknown sample may be identified by comparing the melting point with a list of unknowns in Table 1C-1. Report the melting point range and the identity of the unknown solid. Dispose of the capillary tube in a glass disposal container and return any unused solid to the instructor.

Table 1C-1   Melting Points of Selected
Organic Solids

Organic compound	Melting point (°C)
Benzophenone	48
2-Naphthaldehyde	60
Benzhydrol	68
Vanillin	80
Benzil	95
o-Toluic acid	104
4-Hydroxyacetophenone	109
4-Hydroxybenzaldehyde	115
Benzoic acid	122
trans-Cinnamic acid	133
3-Nitrobenzoic acid	140
2-Nitrobenzoic acid	146
Adipic acid	153
Camphor	178
p-Anisic acid	184

Exercise C.3: Mixed Melting Point

Obtain two vials from the instructor: one will be a sample of cinnamic acid and the other will be an unknown, which will be either cinnamic acid or urea. Record the number of the unknown in your lab notebook. Measure the melting points of cinnamic acid and the other sample and record the melting points in your lab notebook. Use a spatula to transfer 1–2 mg each of cinnamic acid and the unknown solid to a pestle. With a mortar, grind the solids together to mix thoroughly. Measure and record the melting point of the mixture in your lab notebook. Determine whether the unknown is cinnamic acid or urea. Justify your conclusions.

Safety First!

Always wear eye protection in the laboratory.

Questions

1. A student measures the melting point of benzoic acid and reports the melting point in the lab notebook as 122°C. Explain what the student did wrong.

2. Two substances obtained from different sources each melt at 148–150°C. Are they the same? Explain.

3. A substance melts sharply at 135°C. Is it a pure compound? Explain.

4. Benzoic acid and 2-naphthol each melt at 122°C. A sample of unknown solid melts around 122°C. The solid is either benzoic acid or 2-naphthol. Describe a method to determine the identity of the unknown compound.

5. Explain why atmospheric pressure affects boiling points of liquids, but does not affect melting points of solids.

6. Refer to the temperature vs. composition diagram of the phenol/diphenylamine binary system (Figure 1C-1). Estimate the melting point range for a mixture of 85 mol percent phenol/15 mol percent diphenylamine.

7. Do impurities always lower the melting point of an organic compound? Explain.

Technique D: Boiling Points

Introduction

Boiling point is a useful physical property for identifying pure liquids as well as for evaluating the purity of a substance. The boiling point of a liquid is defined as the temperature at which its vapor pressure equals atmospheric pressure. Vapor pressure is a measure of the tendency of molecules to escape from the surface of a liquid. Liquids with higher vapor pressures have lower boiling points than liquids with lower vapor pressures.

The boiling point of a liquid can be measured using a capillary tube as described in Exercises D.1 and D.2. Alternately, the boiling point can be measured during miniscale distillation (Technique G). The temperature at which most of the material distills is recorded as the boiling point. The barometric pressure at the time of the distillation should be recorded, so that a correction can be applied to determine the normal boiling point. The normal boiling point is the boiling point when atmospheric pressure is 1 atmosphere (760 torr) at sea level. Reference books list normal boiling points unless indicated otherwise.

Boiling point varies with atmospheric pressure and with elevation. For example, in Denver, at 5,280 feet, boiling points of common solvents are 4–5°C lower than at sea level. The atmospheric pressure may vary by a few degrees from day to day (or hour to hour) because of weather changes and passage of weather fronts. These differences must be taken into account when comparing boiling points measured in different labs and measured at different times. In general, a correction to the boiling point can be made by allowing approximately 0.35°C per 10 torr deviation from 760 torr (the standard pressure) in the vicinity of 760 torr.

It is also possible to estimate the boiling point of a substance at various pressures using a pressure-temperature nomograph. For example, the reported normal boiling point of an organic liquid is 78.3°C. The nomograph in Figure 1D-1 can be used to determine the boiling point of this liquid in a lab where the atmospheric pressure is 650 torr. A straight line is drawn between the reported normal boiling point (78.3°C) and the pressure (650 torr). The extension of this line crosses the ΔT correction axis at 4°C. At 650 torr this liquid is predicted to boil at 74.3°C (78.3° – 4°C). If the normal boiling point is known, the expected boiling point can be estimated at any desired reduced pressure as low as 600 torr.

The nomograph may also be used to correct an observed (or measured) boiling point to the boiling point at 760 torr (the reported or normal boiling point). To do this, draw a straight line between the pressure and the temperature corresponding to the observed boiling point. The extension of this line intersects the correction factor that must be added to the observed boiling point. For example, the boiling point of a liquid that boils at 122°C in a lab where the ambient pressure is 685 torr would be reported as 125°C (observed boiling point + ΔT = 122°C + 3°C = 125° C).

Intermolecular Attractions

The boiling point of an organic liquid depends upon molecular properties. Boiling points increase with increasing molecular weight in a homologous series of molecules, e.g., pentane < hexane < heptane << decane. This phenomenon is explained in part by the fact that larger molecules have greater intermolecular attractions and require more heat to vaporize. Another trend is the increase in boiling point with decreasing branching of isomeric molecules, if the functional groups are the same. This is due to decreased surface area and intermolecular attractions for more highly branched molecules, e.g., 2,2-dimethylpropane < 2-methylbutane < pentane. For molecules of similar molecular weights, boiling points increase with increasing polarity of the molecules,

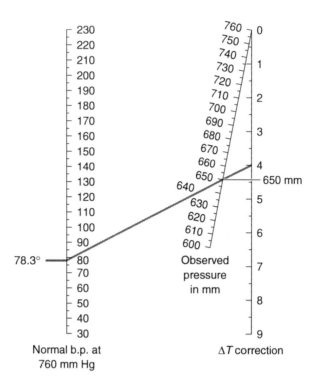

Figure 1D-1

Nomograph

e.g., pentane < 2-butanone < 1-butanol < propanoic acid. More polar molecules have stronger intermolecular forces of attraction. Molecules of similar molecular weight that can hydrogen-bond have even stronger intermolecular interactions.

How to Do a Microscale Boiling Point Determination

Use a syringe to inject 3–5 µL of liquid sample into a capillary tube. Centrifuge, if necessary, to get the entire sample to the bottom of the capillary. Prepare a bell by drawing a melting point capillary tube over a micro burner to make a very fine capillary. Cut a small length of this and carefully seal at one end to make a bell top. (See Figure 1D-2.) Place the bell capillary, sealed end up, into the melting point capillary containing the liquid. Centrifuge, if necessary, to force the bell down to the bottom of the capillary and into the liquid. The open end of the bell should be straight, resulting from a careful break using a file. Ideally, the bell should be about 1½ times the height of the sample liquid. Place the entire system in a heating device, such as that used for melting point measurements (e.g., Mel-Temp, Thomas-Hoover, or similar system). Apply heat until a rapid and steady stream of bubbles flows from the inverted capillary. Stop heating and watch the flow of bubbles. Bubbling will stop and the liquid will flow back up into the inverted capillary. The temperature at which the liquid reenters the bell is recorded as the boiling point.

How to Do a Miniscale Boiling Point Determination

Add 0.3–0.5 mL of the liquid to a small diameter test tube or Craig tube that contains a boiling chip. Clamp the tube in a heat block or sand bath. Suspend the thermometer so that the bottom of the thermometer bulb is 0.5 cm above the level of the liquid and clamp in place. Position the thermometer so that it does not contact the sides of the tube. (See Figure 1D-3.) Gently heat the liquid to boiling. Continue to heat slowly until the refluxing vapor forms a ring of condensate about 1–2 cm above the tip of the bulb.

Figure 1D-2

Microscale boiling
point determination
using a glass bell

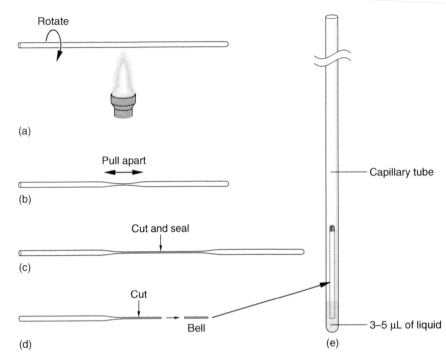

Micro boiling point apparatus

When the temperature stabilizes for at least one minute, record the temperature. This
procedure works well for liquids that boil higher than 50°C.

Microscale

Exercise D.1: Determining the Micro Boiling Point of an
Unknown Liquid

Safety First!

**Always wear eye
protection in the
laboratory.**

Obtain a sample of an unknown liquid from the instructor and record the number of the
unknown in your laboratory notebook. The instructor will demonstrate how to make a
glass bell or one will be supplied. Heat the capillary tube fairly rapidly until a steady
stream of bubbles emerges from the glass bell. Turn down the heat. Watch carefully
until the last bubble collapses and liquid enters the glass bell. Note the temperature. The
temperature at which the liquid reenters the bell is the observed boiling point. Record
this temperature. Because the boiling point of a liquid depends upon pressure, a correction must be applied. To do this, use a nomograph (Figure 1D-1). Record the observed
boiling point and the corrected boiling point. Use Table 1D-1 to determine the identity
of the unknown liquid. Calculate the percent error between the corrected boiling point and
the literature (table) value. (See Appendix B). Report the corrected boiling point, the identity of the unknown, and the percent error. Return any unused sample to the instructor.

Miniscale

Exercise D.2: Determining the Boiling Point of an
Unknown Liquid

Obtain a sample of an unknown liquid from the instructor. Record the unknown number
in your laboratory notebook. Add 0.3–0.5 mL of the liquid and a boiling chip to a small

Figure 1D-3

Apparatus for miniscale
boiling point determi-
nation

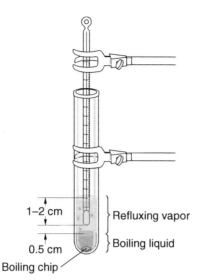

diameter test tube or Craig tube. Clamp the tube in a heat block or sand bath. Suspend the
thermometer so that the bottom of the thermometer bulb is 0.5 cm above the level of the
liquid and clamp in place. Position the thermometer so that it does not contact the sides
of the tube. (See Figure 1D-3.) Gently heat the liquid to boiling. Continue to heat slowly
until the refluxing vapor forms a ring of condensate about 1–2 cm above the tip of the
bulb. When the temperature stabilizes for at least one minute, record the temperature.
Correct the measured boiling point for atmospheric pressure using a nomograph (Figure
1D-1). Use Table 1D-1 to determine the identity of the unknown liquid. Calculate the
percent error between the corrected boiling point and the literature (table) value. Report
the corrected boiling point, the identity of the unknown, and the percent error. (See
Appendix B). Return any unused sample to the instructor.

Safety First!

**Always wear eye
protection in the
laboratory.**

Questions

1. What is the relationship between the volatility of a liquid and its vapor pressure?
2. What is the relationship between the vapor pressure of a liquid and its temperature?
3. Define the terms "boiling point" and "normal boiling point."

Table 1D-1   Boiling Points of Selected
Organic Liquids

Organic compound	Boiling point (°C)
Hexane	69.0
Ethyl acetate	77.1
2-Propanol	82.4
2,3-Dimethylpentane	89.8
1-Propanol	97.4
2-Pentanone	102.0
Toluene	110.6
1-Butanol	117.2
p-Xylene	138.3

4. How is boiling point affected by elevation?

5. A distillate was collected between 78–82°C at sea level. The reported boiling point was 80°C. Comment on the correctness of this report.

6. Explain the effects of polarity of molecules on boiling point.

7. The normal boiling point of toluene (at 760 torr) is 110°C. Use the boiling point nomograph (Figure 1D-1) to determine the boiling point of toluene at 600 torr.

8. A liquid boils at 102°C in a lab in Colorado Springs, where the ambient pressure is 600 torr. What is the corrected boiling point of the liquid?

Technique E: Index of Refraction

Introduction

Light travels at different speeds through different media. It travels slower in air than in a vacuum. It travels slower yet in liquids and solids. As light passes from one medium to another, it also changes directions: this is called refraction as shown in Figure 1E-1.

The index of refraction n is defined as the ratio of sin i to sin r, where i is the angle of incidence and r is the angle of refraction.

$$n = \frac{\sin i}{\sin r}$$

The resulting number, which is unitless, is always greater than 1 since the angle of incident light is always greater than the angle of refracted light as light passes from a less dense to a more dense medium.

The refractive index is an important physical property of organic liquids. The refractive index for many organic liquids can be found in chemical reference books such as the *Handbook of Chemistry and Physics* (CRC) and the *Merck Index*. The literature values are referenced to the **D** line of a sodium lamp at 20°C. A correction factor must be applied if the refractive index (n_{obs}) is measured at temperatures, t, other than 20°C.

$$n_D{}^{20} = n_{obs} + 0.00045 \, (t - 20)$$

The refractive index of a liquid can be measured very accurately. Since impurities affect the refractive index of a liquid, refractometry is a quick and easy method of deter-

Figure 1E-1

Index of refraction

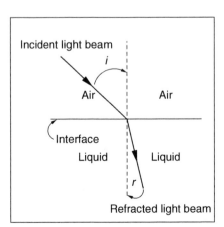

mining the purity of the liquid. Relatively small amounts of sample are required for a measurement (100–250 μL).

How to Use the Abbe Refractometer

The most common instrument for measuring refractive index is the Abbe refractometer, which is shown in Figure 1E-2.

It is important to avoid scratching the prism surface.

To use the refractometer, open the hinged sample prisms and be sure that the stage area (lower prism surface) is clean and dry. Clean, if necessary, using a tissue and alcohol. Add 4 drops of liquid to the stage and move the upper prism over it. Close the prisms. The light source illuminates the upper prism. Adjust the swivel arm of the light source if necessary, then tighten the swivel arm. Turn the large-scale adjustment knob back and forth and look for a split optical field of light and dark that is centered exactly in the crosshairs. This is shown in Figure 1E-3.

Adjust the drum for maximum contrast between the lighter and the darker half circles. Press and hold the scale/sample field switch. The refractive index scale will appear. The upper scale may be read to four decimal places. The scale shown in Figure 1E-4 reads 1.4652. Correct the measured refractive index for temperature, if it differs from 20°C.

Exercise E.1: Measuring the Refractive Index of an Unknown Liquid

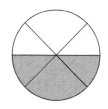

Safety First!

Always wear eye protection in the laboratory.

Obtain a sample of a pure liquid unknown. Record the identification number of the unknown. Place 4 drops of the liquid between the plates of an Abbe refractometer. Measure and record the refractive index of the liquid. Record the ambient temperature. If the

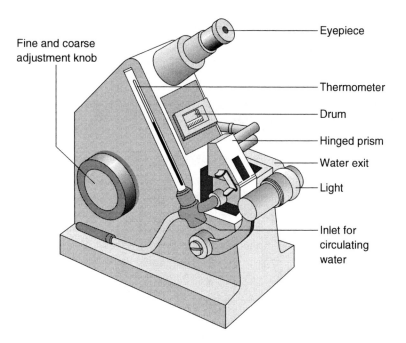

- Eyepiece
- Fine and coarse adjustment knob
- Thermometer
- Drum
- Hinged prism
- Water exit
- Light
- Inlet for circulating water

Figure 1E-2   The Abbe refractometer

Figure 1E-3

Optical field

Figure 1E-4

Refractive index scale

Table 1E-1   Refractive Indices of Selected Organic Liquids

Organic compound	Refractive index (n_D^{20})
Acetonitrile	1.3442
Hexane	1.3751
1-Propanol	1.3850
1-Butanol	1.3993
Cyclohexane	1.4266
Toluene	1.4961

temperature differs from 20°C, apply a correction factor to the refractive index. Record the corrected refractive index. Identify the unknown liquid by comparing the refractive index with a list of unknowns in Table 1E-1. Calculate the percent error between the corrected refractive index and the literature (table) value. Report the corrected refractive index, the identity of the unknown liquid, and the percent error. (Refer to Appendix B). Return any unused sample to the instructor.

Questions

1. A student measures the refractive index of an organic liquid. The value is 1.2821 at 18°C. What is the corrected refractive index?

2. Is refractometry useful in the microscale organic chemistry lab? Explain.

3. Do impurities raise or lower the refractive index of a liquid? Explain.

4. The refractive indices of cyclohexane and toluene are 1.4264 and 1.4967, respectively, at 20°C. A mixture of these two liquids has a refractive index of 1.4563 at that same temperature. Assuming that the relationship between refractive index and concentration is linear, calculate the composition of the mixture.

5. If two samples of organic liquids give the same refractive index reading, are the two liquids the same? Explain.

Technique F: Recrystallization, Filtration, and Sublimation

Introduction to Recrystallization

The physical property that is most useful for purification of solids is differential solubility in an appropriate solvent. When crystals form during a reaction or following an extraction, impurities may become trapped within the crystal lattice or upon the surface of the solid. Washing the crystals with cold solvent can remove adsorbed impurities from the surface, but this process cannot remove the trapped (occluded) impurities. To remove these by recrystallization, it is necessary to redissolve the solid in hot solvent, filter off any insoluble impurities, and then cool the solution to let the material crystallize again.

Theory

Organic solids are usually more soluble in hot solvent than in a comparable volume of cold solvent. In recrystallization, a saturated solution is formed by carefully adding an amount of hot solvent just necessary to dissolve a given amount of solid. A slight excess of solvent may be required for hot gravity filtration used in miniscale experiments. As the solution cools, the solubility of the solid decreases and the solid crystallizes. Unavoidably, some of the solid remains dissolved in the cold solvent, so that not all of the crystals dissolved originally are recovered.

In order to be successfully separated from the impurities in a certain solvent, the solid and the impurities should have differing solubilities. Impurities that remain undissolved in the solvent can be removed by hot gravity filtration of the solution prior to cooling. Impurities that are more soluble will remain in solution after the solid crystallizes. If the impurities and the compound have very similar solubility characteristics, repeated recrystallizations may be required or a different solvent may be required for purification. A crystal of the desired compound (called a "seed" crystal) can be added to the cooling solution to encourage crystallization if crystals fail to form initially.

Solvents for Recrystallization

Selecting a solvent is crucial for the successful recrystallization of an organic solid. An ideal recrystallization solvent should:

- dissolve all of the compound at the boiling point of the solvent.
- dissolve very little or none of the compound when the solvent is at room temperature.
- have different solubilities for the compound and the impurities.
- have a boiling point below the melting point of the compound, so that the compound actually dissolves, not melts, in the hot solvent.
- have a relatively low boiling point (60–100°C) so that the solvent is easily removed from the crystals and the crystals are easy to air dry.
- be nonreactive with the compound, nontoxic, and not have an offensive odor.
- be relatively inexpensive.

A good recrystallization solvent should possess many, if not all, of these properties. The importance of selecting an appropriate recrystallization solvent cannot be overstated.

The compound being recrystallized should dissolve in a reasonable amount of hot solvent but be insoluble in the cold solvent. Recall the adage, **"like dissolves like."** Polar compounds will dissolve in polar solvents, but not in nonpolar solvents. The opposite is true for nonpolar compounds. If the polarities of the compound and the solvent are too similar, the compound will be readily soluble in that solvent and will not crystallize. The compound and the solvent cannot have radically different polarities, or the compound will not dissolve at all. This implies that the compound and the solvent should have somewhat different—but not totally different—polarities. It is obvious that an understanding of polarity is crucial to the selection of a recrystallization solvent.

Polarity is determined by dipole moments of substances. Compounds that contain only carbon and hydrogen are nonpolar. This includes compounds such as alkanes, alkenes, alkynes, and aromatic compounds. Somewhat more polar are ethers and halogenated compounds, followed by ketones and esters. More polar yet are alcohols. This trend is summarized in Table 1F-1.

Factors that influence polarity and solubility of an organic compound are molecular weight and proportion of hydrocarbon in the molecule. Compounds with higher molecular weight are less soluble in general than those with lower molecular weight with the same functional group. The higher the proportion of hydrocarbon to functional group within the molecule, the less polar the compound.

Common recrystallization solvents listed in Table 1F-2 are arranged in order of decreasing solvent polarity, as measured by the dielectric constant. Dielectric constant

Table 1F-1   Classes of Organic Solvents and Examples Used for Recrystallization

Polarity	Class	Example
Most Polar	Alcohols	Methanol, ethanol, 2-propanol
	Ketones	Acetone, 2-butanone
	Esters	Ethyl acetate
	Halogenated alkanes	1, 2-dichloroethane
	Ethers	Diethyl ether, tetrahydrofuran
	Aromatic compounds	Toluene
Least Polar	Alkanes	Hexane, petroleum ether

is a measure of a solvent's ability to moderate the force of attraction between oppositely charged particles (standard = 1.0 for a vacuum).

Chemical reference books, such as the *Handbook of Chemistry and Physics* or the *Merck Index*, are sources of valuable information about solubility. The abbreviations that are used are "i" (indicating that the compound is insoluble), "s" (soluble), "δ" (slightly soluble), "h" (soluble in hot solvent), and "v" (very soluble). A solvent that is listed as slightly soluble or soluble in hot solvent should be a good recrystallization solvent for that compound. Sometimes the handbook will give the exact solubility of a compound in a given solvent. The units of solubility are typically given as grams of compound dissolved per 100 mL of solvent. Unless otherwise noted, the solubilities are measured at 25°C. If solubility information is available, it is possible to calculate the relative amount of solvent needed to dissolve a given amount of compound.

The best way to be certain that a solvent will be a good recrystallization solvent is to try it and see! Test the solvent on a small amount of the compound. If that solvent doesn't dissolve the crystals when hot, or if it dissolves the crystals at room temperature, try another solvent. Keep trying until you find a solvent that dissolves the compound when the solvent is hot, but not when the solvent is cold.

Since it is usually easier to use a single solvent than a solvent pair, it is well worth the time and effort to try to find a single solvent for recrystallization. However, sometimes it happens that no solvent is found that will dissolve the compound when hot, but not when cold. In this case, a solvent pair must be used. A solvent pair consists of two miscible solvents, which have rather different polarities. A solvent pair then consists of two solvents, one in which the compound is soluble, the other in which the compound is insoluble. The most common solvent pair is ethanol-water.

Recrystallization using a single solvent is done by dissolving the compound in the **minimum amount of hot solvent,** filtering any insoluble impurities, then letting the solution cool to room temperature. The rate at which the crystals form affects the purity of the crystals. Cooling too rapidly (such as immersing the warm solution in an ice bath) results in the formation of very small crystals that adsorb impurities from the solution. If crystals are too large, solution and impurities can be trapped (occluded) within the crystal lattice. The optimal crystals are obtained by leaving the flask undisturbed until crystallization occurs. When crystals do appear, the mixture should be cooled further in an ice bath to ensure complete crystallization. The crystals are then suction-filtered, rinsed with several small portions of ice cold solvent to remove traces of surface impurities, and allowed to dry.

Frequently, a second crop of crystals can be obtained from the filtrate (called the mother liquor). This entails heating the filtrate solution to reduce the volume, then letting

Table 1F-2   Properties of Common Recrystallization Solvents

Solvent	Boiling point (°C)	Comments	Dielectric constant
Very polar solvent			
Water	100	Good for moderately polar and polar compounds; difficult to remove solvent from crystals	78.5
Polar solvents			
Methanol	65	Can sometimes be used in place of ethanol	33.0
Ethanol	78	Usually used as 95% ethanol; good for relatively nonpolar compounds	24.3
Acetone	60	Low boiling, but inexpensive; 2-butanone has similar properties and a higher boiling point (80°C)	21.2
2-Propanol	82	Inexpensive; good for relatively nonpolar compounds	18.3
Moderately polar solvent			
Ethyl acetate	77	Good for relatively nonpolar compounds	6.0
Nonpolar solvents			
Toluene	110	High boiling point makes it difficult to remove from crystals; good for moderately polar compounds	2.4
Petroleum ether/ Ligroin (high boiling)	90–110	Very flammable; easy to remove from crystals; cheaper than heptane	2.0
Petroleum ether/ Ligroin (medium boiling)	60–90	Also available as "hexanes"; very flammable; easy to remove from crystals; cheaper than heptane; useful in solvent pair recrystallization	2.0
Petroleum ether/ Ligroin (low boiling)	30–60	Also available as "pentanes"; very flammable	2.0
Cyclohexane	81	Good solvent for less polar compounds	1.9
Hexane	69	Good solvent for less polar compounds; useful in solvent pair recrystallization	1.9

the solution cool slowly as crystallization occurs. The crystals obtained from this second crop are usually not as pure as the initial crop. Melting points should be obtained and the purity evaluated before the two crops of crystals are combined. Since impurities usually lower the melting point and increase the melting point range, the measured melting points are good indications of the purity of the crystals.

The purity of the crystals is one measure of the success of a recrystallization procedure. A second measure is the percent recovery, that is, how many grams of pure compound are obtained relative to the amount of the impure crystals. The percent recovery for a recrystallization process can be determined by measuring the mass of the crystals before recrystallization and after. The percent recovery is given by the equation below.

$$\frac{\text{mass of pure crystals}}{\text{mass of impure crystals}} \times 100\% = \text{Percent Recovery}$$

Low percent recoveries may be due to using the wrong solvent, using too much solvent, incomplete crystallization (not enough time or low enough temperature), or inefficient filtration technique. Since the compound usually has some solubility in the cold solvent, there is always some loss of product.

Choosing a Solvent

The first step (and most important step) is choosing a recrystallization solvent or solvent pair. This is necessary whether doing a microscale or a miniscale recrystallization.

General Procedure

You should narrow the choice of solvents by considering the polarity of the compound being recrystallized. For nonpolar compounds, try solvents of moderate polarity. For moderately polar compounds, try solvents of higher polarity, such as water. For polar compounds, try water or solvents of low to moderate polarity. (Refer to Table 1F-2 for solvent polarities.)

Place about 50 mg of the solid (about the tip of a spatula) into a small test tube. Add 1 mL of the solvent to be tested. Mix the contents thoroughly and observe. If most of the solid dissolves at room temperature, the compound is soluble in this solvent and the solvent will not be a good recrystallization solvent. Start over with a new portion of the solid and a new solvent.

If, on the other hand, most of the solid does not dissolve at room temperature, gently heat the test tube to boiling in a sand bath or water bath. Observe.

- If the solid dissolves in the hot solvent, the solvent will be a good recrystallization solvent.
- If only some of the solid dissolves, try adding another 1 mL portion of the solvent and heating in a sand bath or water bath. If more of the solid dissolves, the compound is slightly soluble and this solvent may work as a recrystallization solvent. Add enough **hot** solvent to dissolve all of the crystals. Then place the test tube in an ice bath. If many crystals form, this solvent will be good for recrystallization.
- If the solid does not at least partially dissolve in the hot solvent, the compound is insoluble in the hot solvent and the solvent will not be a good recrystallization solvent. Start over with a new portion of the solid and a new solvent.

This process is illustrated in Figure 1F-1.

Choosing a Solvent Pair

If no solvent is found that will dissolve the compound when hot but not cold, you must perform a solvent-pair recrystallization. This is easier to do if accurate and detailed notes have been recorded. Select a solvent that dissolved the compound and a different solvent that failed to dissolve the compound. **Remember that the two solvents selected must be miscible.** This means they mix in all proportions, such as ethanol and water. To ensure that the two solvents selected are miscible, put 1-mL portions of each solvent in a test tube and shake. If the solution is homogenous (one phase, clear), the solvents are miscible. If two liquid phases appear, the solvents are immiscible: they cannot be used for a solvent-pair recrystallization.

To test the solvent pair, place about 100 mg of the solid in a test tube. Add dropwise the hot solvent in which the compound is more soluble. Add just enough hot solvent to dissolve the solid, no more. Then add dropwise the hot solvent in which the compound is less soluble. If the solution turns cloudy due to the crystallization of the solid, this

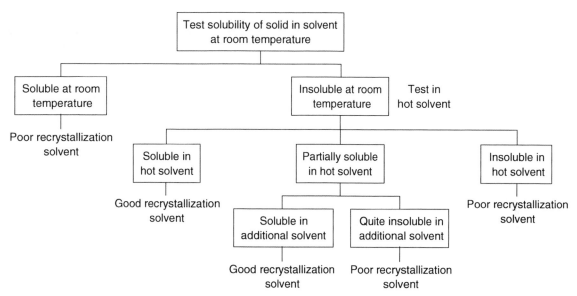

Figure 1F-1　Flow scheme for determining the suitability of a solvent for recrystallization of an organic solid

will be an acceptable solvent pair to use for recrystallization. Once the solvent or solvent system has been determined, proceed with the recrystallization process.

How to Do a Microscale Recrystallization

Microscale Single-Solvent Recrystallization

Microscale single-solvent recrystallization should be used to recrystallize 50 mg to 300 mg of material. Put the crude crystals into a 10-mL Erlenmeyer flask that contains a boiling chip. With a pipet, add approximately 0.2–0.3 mL aliquots of the chosen hot solvent. After each addition of solvent, swirl the crystals and heat the solution on a warm sand bath or heat block. Continue to add the hot solvent until the entire solid has dissolved. Be patient. Don't heat the solution too strongly or the solvent will boil away. Adjust the temperature of the heat source to keep the solution just under the boiling point of the solvent. If there is still undissolved solid, skip ahead to the next paragraph. Otherwise, continue. When the solid has dissolved, remove the Erlenmeyer flask from the sand bath and set it aside to cool to room temperature undisturbed. A large beaker packed with a paper towel or packing material works well to insulate the flask. Place the Erlenmeyer flask down into the beaker. After 10–15 minutes or when the flask is at room temperature, place the flask in a beaker filled with ice. Let the flask stand 5–10 minutes or until the flask feels cold to the touch. Place a small beaker of solvent in the ice bath to cool. If crystallization does not occur even after the solution is cold, scratch the inside of the flask with a glass rod or add a crystal of product (a seed crystal) to the solution. If crystallization still does not occur, reduce the volume of solution and let it cool to room temperature. After crystallization is complete, suction filter the crystals using a Hirsch funnel and small filter flask. Rinse the crystals sparingly with several drops of the ice-cold solvent and air dry the crystals.

Hood!

Microscale filtration apparatus
(See Figure 1F-3).

If further addition of the hot solvent does not dissolve more of the solid, the solid particles are probably insoluble impurities. If this is the case, it is necessary to filter the mixture. Prepare a Pasteur filter pipet (a Pasteur pipet fitted with a cotton plug). Hold the pipet over the flask for a minute or two to warm (to prevent crystallization within the pipet). Obtain a clean 10-mL Erlenmeyer flask or a 5-mL conical vial. Add 5–10 drops of the hot solvent to the flask or vial and set it on the warm sand bath or heat block. Squeeze on the bulb to remove the air and place the pipet in the mixture. Slowly release the bulb to draw up the solution into the Pasteur pipet. Try not to draw up any of the solid impurities. Transfer the solution to a clean flask or vial. Any solid that gets drawn up in the pipet will stick to the cotton. (See Figure 1F-4.) The pipet may be rinsed with one or two small portions of solvent. Sometimes crystals form immediately upon contact with the container. If this happens, add more hot solvent until all of the solid dissolves. Then remove the container from the heat source, allow it to cool to room temperature, and proceed as above.

Hot filtration should also be done if the solution is highly colored (when the pure compound is white!). In this case, it will be necessary to add a small amount of decolorizing carbon (such as Norit or charcoal) to the warm (not boiling!) solution. Decolorizing carbon has a very large surface area that enables it to adsorb colored impurities. To use decolorizing carbon, add 5–6 more drops of solvent and let the solution cool a little below the boiling point so as to avoid splattering. Add a spatula-tip full or less of the decolorizing carbon and swirl. Heat the black mixture for several minutes, then filter using a filter pipet. Transfer the clear solution to a clean container and proceed as described above. If small particles of carbon can be seen, it may be necessary to refilter using a new Pasteur pipet.

Microscale Solvent-Pair Recrystallization

This procedure should be used if no single solvent is found that will work for the recrystallization procedure.

Hood!

Heat two small flasks, each containing one of the solvents to be used for the recrystallization. Place the crystals in a 10-mL Erlenmeyer flask or 5-mL conical vial. With a pipet, add dropwise the hot solvent that was found to best dissolve the compound. Swirl after each addition of hot solvent. When the crystals are dissolved, add dropwise the hot solvent that does not dissolve the compound. Observe carefully after each addition. Continue adding the solvent until the solution appears cloudy or crystal formation is observed. This is called the "cloud point." Then add 1–2 drops more of the first solvent to just redissolve the crystals and cause the cloudiness to disappear. Remove the container from the heat source and allow to cool to room temperature, undisturbed. Chill further in an ice bath, then suction filter the crystals. Wash with several small portions of ice-cold solvent (the solvent in which the compound is insoluble!). Air dry the crystals or place in a drying oven.

If some of the solid does not dissolve during addition of the first hot solvent, remove the solid impurities by drawing up the solution with a Pasteur filter pipet. Transfer the solution to a clean vial or Erlenmeyer flask. Add a little more of the first hot solvent if necessary. Then add the second hot solvent dropwise until the solution appears cloudy.

If no crystals are obtained upon cooling, reheat the solution. Again add dropwise the hot solvent that does not dissolve the compound. At the cloud point, cool the solution and wait for crystallization.

Ultra-Microscale Recrystallization and Use of a Craig Tube

Hood!

For very small amounts of product, it is necessary to use a Craig tube for recrystallization. This procedure should be used for recrystallization of less than 50 mg of material.

Place the crude crystals in the bottom of a 1-mL or 2-mL Craig tube. Dissolve the crystals in a minimum amount of hot solvent. Fit the Craig plug into the Craig tube.

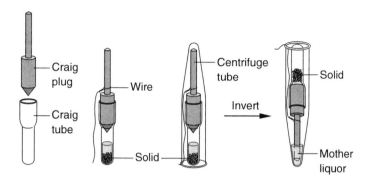

Figure 1F-2

Craig tube recrystallization

Cool the solution to room temperature. Place the tube in a beaker filled with ice to ensure complete precipitation. To prepare the tube for crystallization, wrap a piece of wire around the neck of the Craig tube. (See Figure 1F-2.) The wire must be longer than the centrifuge tube. Fit a centrifuge tube over the Craig tube. Holding the wire firmly, invert the centrifuge tube.

Centrifuge the mixture, making certain that it is balanced. The liquid will be forced down into the tip of the centrifuge tube, leaving the crystals on the plug. Carefully remove the Craig tube from the centrifuge tube using the wire "handle." Over a clean watch glass, disassemble the Craig tube. Scrape the crystals onto the watch glass and let them dry thoroughly before weighing or taking a melting point. This process is illustrated in Figure 1F-2.

How to Do a Miniscale Recrystallization

Miniscale Single-Solvent Recrystallization

This procedure should be used for recrystallizing 300 mg or more of a solid. Transfer the impure solid into a 10-mL or larger Erlenmeyer flask. Heat the solvent on a hot sand bath or steam bath in the hood. Most organic solvents are flammable, so use extreme caution when heating. Add the minimum amount of the hot solvent required to dissolve the crude crystals. Swirl to dissolve, while heating. Continue to add small portions of the hot solvent until all of the solid dissolves. If it becomes apparent that insoluble impurities are present, any solids that do not dissolve may be removed by hot gravity filtration. Obtain a second Erlenmeyer flask and add 1–2 mL of the hot solvent. Set a stemless funnel fitted with a piece of fluted filter paper (see Figure 1F-6) on top of the Erlenmeyer. Set the funnel in an iron ring or place a paper clip between the funnel and neck of the Erlenmeyer. Heat the flask and funnel so hot vapors fill the system. To keep the solid in solution, add 1–2 mL of the hot solvent to the first Erlenmeyer flask. Add a spatula-tip full of decolorizing carbon if the solution is deeply colored. Keeping everything hot, pour the solution through the filter paper in small batches. Continue pouring until all of the solution is transferred. The solution should be clear and colorless. If crystallization occurs in the flask or filter paper, add more of the hot solvent to dissolve the crystals. When all the solid is dissolved, remove the solution from the heat and let it stand undisturbed. Cool to room temperature (about 15–20 minutes). After crystallization occurs, place the flask in an ice bath to ensure complete crystallization. If no crystals form, scratch the inside of the flask with a glass rod or add a seed crystal. If crystallization still doesn't occur, add a boiling chip and heat the solution in the hood to reduce the volume. After the solution has been cooled in the ice bath, filter by suction filtration, washing with several small portions of ice-cold solvent. Dry the crystals on the filter by drawing air through using continued suction or by placing in a drying oven.

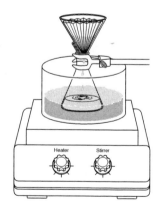

Miniscale Solvent-Pair Recrystallization

This procedure should be used when a single recrystallization solvent cannot be found. Place 300 mg or more of the crude crystals in a 25-mL or larger Erlenmeyer flask. On a hot sand bath or steam bath, heat two flasks containing the solvents. One flask will contain solvent in which the compound is soluble. The other flask will contain solvent in which the compound is insoluble. Add dropwise the solvent in which the compound is soluble. Add just enough to dissolve the compound, no more. Then, add dropwise the solvent in which the compound is less soluble. Observe carefully. Add just enough until the solution turns cloudy (the cloud point) and remains so even after swirling. This is the point at which the crystals are beginning to come out of solution. Now add 1 or 2 drops (no more!) of the solvent in which the compound is soluble. Add just enough to dissipate the cloudiness. Remove the flask from the heat source and let the solution stand undisturbed to cool to room temperature. When crystallization occurs, chill the flask in an ice bath and suction filter the crystals. If crystallization does not occur, scratch the inside of the flask with a glass rod or add a seed crystal. If crystallization still does not occur, heat the solution in the hood. Again add dropwise the hot solvent that does not dissolve the compound. At the cloud point, cool the solution and wait for crystallization. After crystallization occurs, cool the flask in an ice bath and suction filter. Wash the crystals with several small portions of ice-cold solvent (the one in which the compound is insoluble). Allow the crystals to dry before taking a melting point.

If some of the solid does not dissolve during addition of the first hot solvent, filter the insoluble material by gravity filtration and continue.

Important Tips Concerning Recrystallization

1. Use an Erlenmeyer flask in the hood for recrystallization, not a beaker. The solvent can too easily boil away from a beaker or be splashed out.
2. If no precipitate forms even after the solution has been standing in an ice bath, it may be necessary to induce crystallization. Try one or more of the following techniques:
    a. Scratch the inside surface of the Erlenmeyer flask with a glass rod. The scratched glass acts to induce crystallization.
    b. Add a seed crystal of the compound (if available) to the cooled solution. This can act as a template to initiate crystallization.
    c. If neither of the previous suggestions works, it is probable that too much solvent was added initially. Reduce the volume by heating until the solution appears cloudy. This is the point at which crystallization is occurring. Add a few more drops of the hot solvent until the solution is clear, then allow to cool slowly.
    d. If crystals have still not formed, it is possible that the wrong solvent was selected, one in which the compound was too soluble. Evaporate the solvent by boiling, leaving the impure crystals. Then try again with a different solvent.
3. Experimental procedures generally do not specify the exact amount of solvent to use for recrystallization of a crude product. If a volume of solvent is specified, that amount is based on an average yield. If the mass of crystals actually obtained is significantly different from the average yield, the amount of solvent used should be scaled accordingly. **Always use the minimum amount of hot solvent to dissolve the crystals.**
4. Whenever an experimental procedure specifies two solvents (separated by a hyphen) to be used for recrystallization, it implies a solvent-pair recrystallization. The solvent listed first is the solvent in which the compound is soluble. The second solvent is the one in which the compound is insoluble. For example, "recrystallize the solid from ethanol-water" means that the solid is soluble in ethanol and not soluble in water.

Hood!

5. Oils are sometimes obtained instead of crystals. This is a common problem, especially if the solid has a low melting point. An oil can form if the boiling point of the solvent is greater than the melting point of the compound. When the oil solidifies, impurities are trapped within the crystal lattice of the crystals. If this happens, try one or more of the suggestions listed below:

    a. Redissolve the oil by heating gently and let the solution cool back down to room temperature. If an oil starts to re-form, shake the mixture vigorously and cool in an ice bath. Repeat until solidification occurs.

    b. Add a little more solvent to the oil. If using a solvent pair, add a little more of the solvent in which the compound is insoluble. If this doesn't work, try adding a little more of the solvent in which the compound is soluble. Let stand. If a seed crystal is available, add one now.

    c. Triturate the oil. To triturate, add a small amount of a solvent in which the product is expected to be insoluble. With a glass rod, gently mash the oil in the solvent. If impurities in the oil are soluble in the solvent, then the oil may crystallize using this procedure.

    d. If the above methods don't work, start over, using a new solvent for recrystallization. Use a solvent with a lower boiling point.

Introduction to Filtration

Once crystals have formed, they must be separated by the process of filtration. In filtration, a porous barrier, usually filter paper or sintered glass, allows the liquid but not the solid to pass through. The two most important methods of filtration are gravity filtration and suction (vacuum) filtration. Gravity filtration is done when the desired substance is in the solution; the solid (such as decolorizing carbon or a drying agent) is collected on the paper and discarded and the filtrate is collected for further use. Suction filtration is chosen when the desired substance is the solid and it is necessary to isolate it as a dry solid.

How to Do a Microscale Suction Filtration

This technique is used to isolate a dry solid product as in recrystallization. The equipment required is a heavy-walled, sidearm suction flask, filter ring or filter adapter (neoprene), a Hirsch funnel, a piece of appropriately sized filter paper, and a safety trap connected with thick-walled vacuum tubing. The flask should be clamped to avoid breakage (see Figure 1F-3).

The filter paper should be large enough that the holes in the funnel are just covered. If the filter paper selected is too large (larger than the diameter of the funnel), a tight seal cannot be obtained. Additionally, some of the mixture may flow over the unsealed

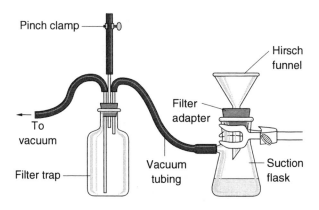

Figure 1F-3
Microscale filtration apparatus

Pinch clamp

Hirsch funnel

Filter adapter

To vacuum

Filter trap

Vacuum tubing

Suction flask

edge and result in loss of product as well as contamination of the filtrate. A small quantity of the solvent to be filtered is used to wet the paper, and suction is applied, usually via a water aspirator. The maximum suction should always be applied, so the aspirator is fully turned on. This procedure prevents solids from getting under the filter paper, which could lead to clogging of the funnel and/or loss of the solid into the filtrate. The mixture to be filtered is swirled and then rapidly poured into the funnel. After the liquid has been drawn through, the resulting crystals are usually washed with a minimum amount of cold solvent. If the solvent is high boiling, traces may be washed out by using a more volatile solvent, as long as it does not dissolve the filtered crystals. Drawing air through the filter for a few minutes further dries the crystals. It is important to remove all of the solvent or the yield and melting point will be inaccurate. It may be necessary to press out the last remnants of the solvent with a spatula by pressing down on the filter cake. The resulting dry, solid product is carefully removed from the filter paper, taking care not to scrape off pieces of the paper fibers and contaminate the product.

A safety trap must be used during the suction filtration to prevent backup of water into the filtrate. This can easily occur if there is a sudden drop in pressure, for example, if nearby aspirators are turned on. **It is also important to break the vacuum connection at the side arm of the suction flask before the aspirator vacuum is turned off or a water backup may occur.**

How to Use a Microscale Filter Pipet

Use of a filter pipet is a quick and easy method for separating a liquid from an unwanted solid, such as a drying agent. Prepare the filter pipet by placing a small piece of cotton or glass wool in the neck of a Pasteur pipet (see Figure 1F-4). Use a piece of wire or an applicator stick to push the cotton down into the tip of the pipet. Draw up the solution to be filtered into the filter pipet. Apply pressure to the pipet bulb and completely force all of the liquid out of the filter pipet into a clean flask. The drying agent or solid impurities will adhere to the cotton. Rinse the filter pipet with fresh solvent and add this rinse to the flask. Alternatively, the solution may be drawn up in a clean Pasteur pipet and drained through the filter pipet.

How to Do a Miniscale Suction Filtration

The procedure for suction filtration is very similar to that of microscale suction filtration. A Büchner funnel is used in place of a Hirsch funnel. The size of the suction flask will depend upon the quantity of solution to be filtered. Because the apparatus tends to be very top-heavy, it should be clamped to a ring stand. The setup is shown in Figure 1F-5.

Place the filter paper in the funnel and pour a little of the solvent through the funnel to wet the filter paper. Turn on the aspirator or vacuum source full force to seal the filter paper to the funnel. Then carefully pour the solution in the center of the funnel. Rinse the reaction flask with a very small amount of the cold solvent for complete transfer. Rinse the crystals with a minimum amount of the cold solvent. Continue to apply vacuum to help dry the crystals. Break the vacuum, then turn off the aspirator. When the crystals are completely dry, carefully scrape the crystals from the filter paper.

How to Do a Miniscale Gravity Filtration

This simple technique requires only a filter paper, a short-stem glass funnel, and a receiving vessel. A stemless funnel is used for hot filtration. The filter paper should be folded into quarters or preferably fluted to maximize the surface area and the rate of flow through it. Fluted filter paper can easily be prepared by folding the filter paper in

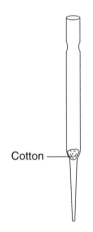

Cotton

Figure 1F-4

Filter pipet

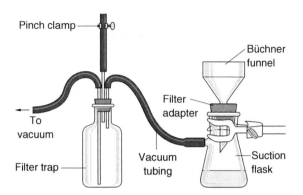

Figure 1F-5

Miniscale suction filtration apparatus

half and then in half again, resulting in quarters. Each of these quarters is folded again to give the fluted paper in eighths. This procedure is illustrated in Figure 1F-6.

Proper choice of the size of filter paper will result in a fluted funnel that fits into the glass funnel and is just slightly below the rim of the funnel. The funnel is held above the collection flask by an iron ring, wire, clay triangle, or paper clip. The funnel should not be flush against the receiving flask; an air space should be provided to avoid slow or incomplete filtration. (See Figure 1F-7.) In some cases it is desirable to preheat both the funnel and filter when filtration of a hot solution or mixture is required. This is most commonly accomplished by placing the glass funnel and filter paper over a hot (boiling) solvent until they are bathed in the hot vapors. Filtration is then quickly carried out. This is to prevent premature crystallization of the solid in the filter paper or stem of the funnel. As noted above, this technique is used primarily to remove undissolved solids during a hot filtration in a recrystallization procedure or to remove a drying agent or decolorizing carbon.

Important Tips Concerning Filtration

1. Always clamp the suction filtration apparatus to a ring stand, so that the apparatus does not tip over.
2. Make sure that the filter paper is just big enough to cover the holes of the funnel. If the paper is too big, solids can get underneath and spill into the flask along with the filtrate.
3. Placing a rubber sheet over the top of the funnel and securing it with a rubber band can help dry the crystals. The suction forces the rubber sheet down on top of the crystals, helping to dry the crystals.
4. Crystals should be thoroughly dried before being carefully scraped off the filter paper. Otherwise, tiny paper fibers will contaminate the crystals.
5. With high-boiling solvents, it is best to let the crystals air dry overnight. To do this, carefully lift the filter paper and crystals out of the funnel and place on a large watch glass.

Introduction to Sublimation

Some solids, which have high vapor pressures, do not melt into a liquid, but are converted directly to a gas. The process of converting from a solid phase into a gas phase without going through the liquid phase is called **sublimation.** A familiar example of sublimation is dry ice (solid CO_2). A piece of dry ice sitting on the lab bench will disappear into a fog of carbon dioxide vapor, leaving no trace of liquid. Why does this occur? As a solid is heated, its vapor pressure increases. At the melting-point temperature, if the vapor pressure of the solid is less than ambient pressure, the solid will melt into a liquid.

Figure 1F-6

Steps for fluting filter paper

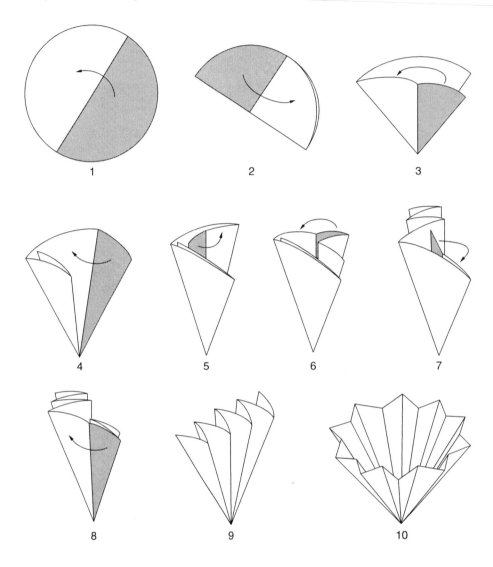

Figure 1F-7

Miniscale hot gravity filtration

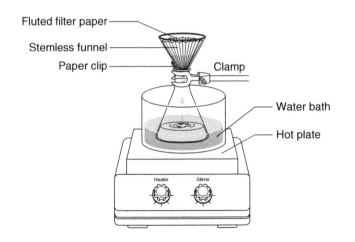

This is the case for most organic solids. If, however, the vapor pressure of the solid is greater than ambient pressure, the solid will sublime. This is the case with dry ice.

Organic compounds that sublime tend to be relatively nonpolar and fairly symmetrical. They have small dipole moments and relatively low molecular weight. Examples of compounds that sublime under reduced pressure are shown in Table 1F-3. Structures of these compounds are shown in Figure 1F-8. Compounds with higher vapor pressures at their melting points are easier to sublime.

Because few organic compounds have high enough vapor pressures to sublime at atmospheric pressure, this technique is generally performed under reduced pressure using a water aspirator, house vacuum line, or vacuum pump. For example, caffeine melts at 235°C, but sublimes at only 51°C if the pressure is reduced to 15 torr. Sublimation is relatively simple to perform. The sample to be sublimed is placed in the bottom of a tube or flask that is fitted with an inner tube (called a cold finger). The cold finger is cooled with running water or filled with ice. The tube or flask is evacuated and the sample is heated in a sand bath to a temperature just below its melting point. As it is heated, the sample will condense onto the cold finger, where it will resolidify, leaving the non-volatile impurities in the bottom of the sublimation chamber. When sublimation is complete, the vacuum is released slowly and the cold finger carefully withdrawn to avoid displacing the crystals. Examples of sublimation setups are shown in Figure 1F-9.

Recrystallization and sublimation are both methods of purifying organic solids. Which technique you choose will depend upon the organic compound you are trying to

Table 1F-3   Sublimation Data for Selected Organic Compounds

Compound	Melting point (°C)	Vapor pressure (torr) at melting point
Hexachloroethane	186	780
Camphor	179	370
Anthracene	218	41
1,4-Dichlorobenzene	53	8.5
1,4-Dibromobenzene	87	9

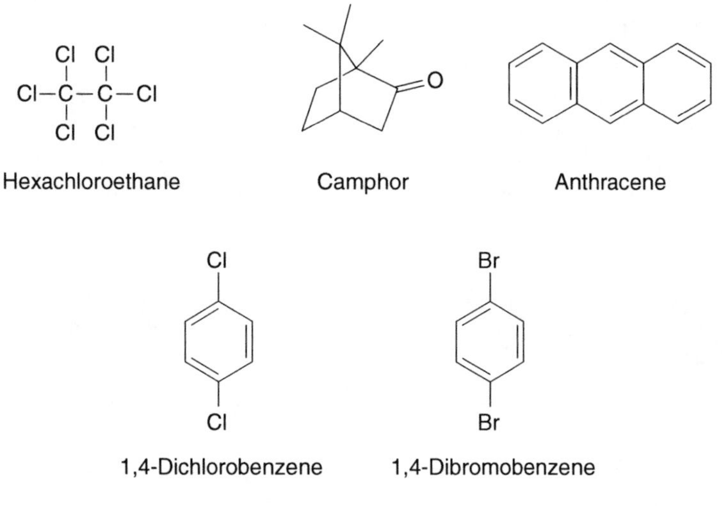

Hexachloroethane   Camphor   Anthracene

1,4-Dichlorobenzene   1,4-Dibromobenzene

Figure 1F-8

Structures of compounds in Table 1F-3

Figure 1F-9

Microscale and mini-scale sublimation setups

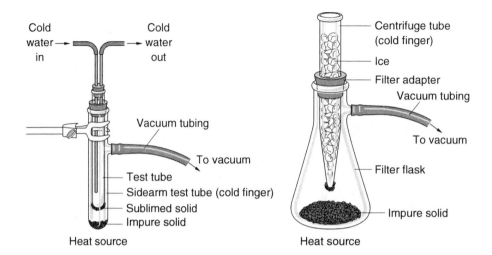

purify and the nature of the impurities present. In general, recrystallization is more applicable for a wider range of compounds, but sublimation is an alternative for those specific compounds that have high vapor pressures at their melting points.

Microscale

Safety First!

Always wear eye protection in the laboratory.

Exercise F.1: Recrystallizing an Impure Solid

Obtain a sample of an impure solid from your instructor. The solid will be either acetanilide or benzoic acid. Record the sample number in your lab notebook.

Add 5–6 mL of water to a 10-mL Erlenmeyer flask containing a boiling chip and heat to boiling on a sand bath. Weigh out 100 mg of the crude solid and place in a 10-mL Erlenmeyer flask that contains a boiling chip. Add approximately 1 mL of hot water to the solid and swirl. Keeping the solution hot, use a pipet to add small aliquots (about 0.1 mL) of hot solvent and swirl after each addition. Continue to add solvent until all the solid dissolves. If necessary, filter off insoluble impurities using a filter pipet.

When the solid has dissolved, remove the flask from the heat, place a small watch glass on top of the flask, and allow it to cool. When the flask is at room temperature, place the flask in an ice bath for 5–10 minutes to ensure complete crystallization. If an oil forms, add a little more water, heat to boiling, and cool. If crystallization does not occur, scratch the inside of the flask with a glass rod. If necessary, place the flask on a hot sand bath or water bath and reduce the volume by boiling off excess solvent.

When crystallization is complete, vacuum filter the crystals using a Hirsch funnel. Wash the crystals with 0.1–0.2 mL of ice-cold water. When the crystals are completely dry, record the weight and the melting point. Calculate the percent recovery. Transfer the pure crystals into a labeled vial and turn in to the instructor.

Miniscale

Safety First!

Always wear eye protection in the laboratory.

Exercise F.2: Recrystallizing an Impure Solid

Obtain a sample of an impure solid from your instructor. The solid will be either acetanilide or benzoic acid. Record the sample number in your lab notebook.

Add approximately 20–30 mL of water to a 50-mL Erlenmeyer flask and heat to the boiling point on a hot plate. Weigh 500 mg of crude solid and place in a 25-mL Erlenmeyer flask that contains a boiling chip. Add approximately 5 mL of hot water to the solid and swirl. Place the flask on a hot plate and slowly heat to boiling. Add small aliquots (about 0.5–1 mL) of hot water and swirl well after each addition. Continue to add solvent until all the solid dissolves. If the solution is deeply colored, or if the solid is not fully dissolved after the addition of 10–15 mL of hot water, insoluble impurities may be present. Perform a hot gravity filtration (see Figure 1F-7), only if instructed to do so.

When the solid has dissolved, remove the flask from the heat, place a small watch glass on top of the flask, and allow it to cool. When the flask is at room temperature, place the flask in an ice bath for 5–10 minutes to ensure complete crystallization. If an oil forms, add a little more water, heat to boiling, and recool. If crystallization does not occur, scratch the inside of the flask with a glass rod. If necessary, place the flask on a hot plate or steam bath in the hood and reduce the volume by boiling off excess solvent.

When the flask is cold and crystallization is complete, suction filter the crystals. Wash the crystals with small portions of ice-cold water. Air dry the crystals or place in a drying oven. When the crystals are completely dry, record the weight and the melting point. Identify the unknown solid. Calculate the percent recovery. Transfer the pure crystals into a labeled vial and turn in to the instructor.

Exercise F.3: Recrystallizing an Impure Solid with Hot Gravity Filtration

Miniscale

Add approximately 20–25 mL of water to a 125-mL Erlenmeyer flask and heat to the boiling point on a hot plate. Weigh 500 mg of crude acetanilide or benzoic acid and place in a 25-mL Erlenmeyer flask that contains a boiling chip. Add approximately 5 mL of hot water to the solid and swirl. Place the flask on a hot plate and slowly heat to boiling. Add small aliquots (about 1 mL) of hot water and swirl well after each addition. Continue to add solvent until all the acetanilide dissolves. If the solution is colored, the solid contains impurities and it is necessary to do a hot gravity filtration.

Safety First!

Always wear eye protection in the laboratory.

Remove the flask from the heat; cool to slightly below the boiling point (or the solution will splatter when the charcoal is added). Add a spatula-tip full of activated charcoal to the solution and swirl. Add additional charcoal to remove the color from the solution, but don't add more charcoal than necessary, since its high surface area adsorbs the solid, reducing the percent recovery. Add 1–2 mL additional hot water to the flask and reheat the solution to the boiling point.

As the solution is reheating, set up another 25-mL Erlenmeyer flask containing a boiling chip with a stemless funnel and fluted filter paper. Pour 1–2 mL of hot water through the funnel to fill the flask with solvent vapors and put the flask on a hot plate. Pour the solution in small batches through the filtration system. The solution should be colorless. If it is not, add additional charcoal and repeat the filtration process. When the filtration is complete, boil off 2–3 mL of the excess solvent added. Then remove the flask from the heat, place a small watch glass on top of the flask, and allow it to cool. When the flask is at room temperature, place the flask in an ice bath for 5–10 minutes to ensure complete crystallization. If an oil forms, add a little more water, heat to boiling, and cool. If crystallization does not occur, scratch the inside of the flask with a glass rod or add a seed crystal of the solid. If necessary, place the flask on a hot plate and reduce the volume by boiling off excess solvent.

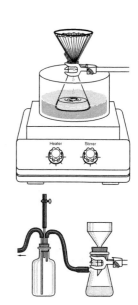

When the flask is cold and crystallization is complete, suction filter the crystals. Wash the crystals with small portions of ice-cold water. Air dry the crystals or place them in a drying oven. When the crystals are completely dry, record the weight and the melting point. Identify the unknown solid. Calculate the percent recovery. Transfer the pure solid into a labeled vial and turn in to the instructor.

Microscale

Exercise F.4: Purifying an Unknown Solid by Solvent-Pair Recrystallization

Obtain an unknown solid from the instructor. The solid will be phenanthrene (melting point = 100°C), anthracene (melting point = 218°C), or *trans*-cinnamic acid (melting point = 133°C). Weigh approximately 100 mg of the solid into a 25-mL Erlenmeyer flask containing a boiling chip. Record the exact mass used. Add 0.5 mL of hot 95% ethanol to the solid, and swirl to dissolve. Heat the solution on a hot plate, but do not heat so strongly that the solvent boils away. While keeping the solution warm, dissolve the solid in a minimum amount of hot 95% ethanol by adding it from a pipet dropwise until the solid just dissolves to produce a clear solution. Add hot water dropwise until the solution becomes cloudy. Then add a few more drops of hot 95% ethanol until the solution is clear. Remove the flask from the heat. Let cool to room temperature, undisturbed, to induce crystallization. Chill the flask in an ice bath. Isolate the crystals by suction filtration, rinsing the crystals with a minimum amount of ice-cold water. Air dry. Weigh the crystals and calculate the percent recovery. Measure the melting point and identify the unknown solid.

Microscale

Exercise F.5: Sublimation of Caffeine

Safety First!

Always wear eye protection in the laboratory.

Weigh about 200 mg of impure caffeine and record the mass. Assemble the sublimation chamber from a 20 × 150-mm sidearm test tube and a 15 × 125-cm test tube, as shown in Figure 1F-9. The inner test tube (the cold finger) may be filled with ice chips or it may be cooled with running water. If using water cooling, fit the cold finger with a two-holed neoprene adapter in which glass tubing has been inserted. Attach rubber tubing to the glass tubing; connect one piece of rubber tubing to the cold water faucet and insert the other piece of rubber tubing firmly into the drain. Put the impure caffeine sample in the bottom of the sidearm test tube and clamp in place. Attach thick-walled rubber tubing to the sidearm. Connect the tubing to a safety trap and connect the trap to an aspirator or house vacuum. Fit the cold finger with neoprene adapter into the sidearm test tube. Fill the cold finger with ice chips, or connect the rubber tubing and gently turn on the cold water. Turn on the aspirator or house vacuum. Heat gently using a warm sand bath or heat block. As the sample is heated, crystals will form on the cold finger. Continue heating until sublimation is complete and no more crystals form on the cold finger. Remove the heat source and allow the apparatus to cool to room temperature. **Cautiously break the vacuum at the trap.** Turn off the cold water, if necessary. **Very carefully, remove the cold finger** from the sublimation chamber, so as not to dislodge any of the crystals. Scrape the crystals onto a tared piece of weighing paper and reweigh. Record the mass of pure caffeine.

   An alternative sublimation chamber can be made from a 125-mL filter flask rather than a sidearm test tube.

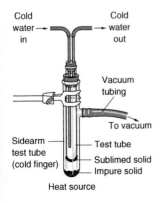

Cold water in → ← Cold water out

Vacuum tubing

To vacuum

Sidearm test tube (cold finger) — Test tube

Sublimed solid
Impure solid

Heat source

Exercise F.6: Sublimation of Caffeine

Miniscale

Weigh about 500 mg of impure caffeine and record the exact mass used. Assemble the sublimation chamber from a flask and cold finger, as shown in Figure 1F-9. Put the impure caffeine sample in the bottom of the flask and clamp in place. Attach thick-walled rubber tubing to the vacuum outlet. Connect the tubing to a trap and connect the trap to an aspirator or house vacuum. Attach rubber tubing to the water inlet and outlet of the cold finger and gently turn on the cold water. Turn on the aspirator or house vacuum. Heat the sublimation chamber gently using a warm sand bath or oil bath. As the sample is heated, crystals will form on the cold finger. Continue heating until sublimation is complete and no more crystals form on the cold finger. Remove the heat source and allow the apparatus to cool to room temperature. **Cautiously break the vacuum at the trap** and, if necessary, turn off the cold water. **Very carefully, remove the cold finger** from the sublimation chamber, so as not to dislodge any of the crystals. Scrape the crystals onto a tared piece of weighing paper and reweigh. Record the mass of pure caffeine.

Safety First!

Always wear eye protection in the laboratory.

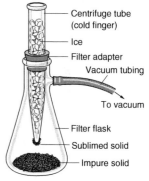

Centrifuge tube (cold finger)
Ice
Filter adapter
Vacuum tubing
To vacuum
Filter flask
Sublimed solid
Impure solid
Heat source

Questions

1. List the most important criteria for selecting a recrystallization solvent.

2. When is it necessary to use a solvent-pair recrystallization?

3. Why should the recrystallization solvent have a fairly low boiling point?

4. What problems might occur if crystallization occurs too rapidly?

5. Why should the recrystallization mixture be cooled in an ice bath prior to filtering?

6. Why should the boiling point of the solvent be lower than the melting point of the compound being recrystallized?

7. What is a "cloud point"? What does it signify when doing a solvent-pair recrystallization?

8. Sometimes crystallization does not occur, even after cooling the solution in the ice bath. Describe the probable cause of this problem and explain what steps might be taken to induce crystallization.

9. After recrystallization, a student obtained a very low percent recovery of a solid. Describe a probable cause of the low yield and explain what steps might be taken to increase the recovery.

10. A compound has a solubility in ethanol of 4.24 g/100 mL at 78°C and of 0.86 g/100 mL at 0°C.

    a. What volume of hot ethanol will be necessary to dissolve 50 mg of the compound? (Assume no impurities.)

    b. How much of the compound will remain dissolved in the solvent after recrystallization is complete? (Assume no loss of crystals due to faulty technique!)

    c. What is the maximum percent recovery that could be attained?

11. Is it better to use a long-stem or short-stem funnel when doing a hot gravity filtration? Explain.

12. During a suction filtration, what are the consequences of using a filter paper that is larger than the funnel diameter and using one that is too small? What are the consequences for the use of each?

13. What problem occurs if a student turns off the aspirator before detaching the tubing at a connecting point?

14. What criteria should you use to determine whether recrystallization or sublimation will be a better method of purification?

15. Why is sublimation usually done under reduced pressure conditions?

16. An organic solid has a vapor pressure of 900 torr at its melting point (100°C). Explain how you would purify this compound.

17. Another organic solid has a vapor pressure of 25 torr at its melting point (100°C). Explain how you would purify this compound.

18. Hexachloroethane has a vapor pressure of 780 torr at its melting point, 186°C. What difficulties might be encountered when attempting to measure the melting point of this compound in a melting point determination apparatus?

Technique G: Distillation and Reflux

Introduction to Simple Distillation

Distillation is a process used to purify liquids. **Simple distillation** is the condensation of vapors from a boiling liquid and collection of the condensed vapors in a receiving vessel as shown by the diagram in Figure 1G-1.

Following the path of a typical liquid molecule in the distilling flask, the molecule circulates in the solution until it passes into the vapor state due to heating. Once in the vapor state, the molecule returns to the solution in the flask or travels up through the still head and over through the condenser to the receiving vessel. Distillation of ocean water to furnish pure water is an example of a commercial application of simple distillation.

Theory of Simple Distillation

A pure liquid, such as acetic acid, exhibits a vapor pressure that is temperature dependent. At ambient temperature and pressure, the aroma of acetic acid can be detected due to molecules in the vapor state above the surface of the liquid. Upon heating, the vapor pressure increases slowly and then more rapidly near the boiling point, as shown in Figure 1G-2. Vapor-pressure curves of other common liquids are also shown in the diagram. More volatile liquids, such as diethyl ether, exhibit higher vapor pressures at all temperatures than less volatile liquids.

Distillation of a pure liquid occurs at the boiling point of the liquid. The boiling point is defined as the temperature at which the vapor pressure above the solution is equal to the atmospheric pressure (or internal pressure in vacuum distillation). Normal boiling point is defined as the boiling point of a pure liquid when the atmospheric pressure is one atmosphere (760 torr).

The temperature reading of the thermometer in the still head remains at room temperature until the first vapors of liquid contact the bulb. The temperature rises rapidly until it reaches the boiling point of the liquid, then remains constant as long as distillate condenses in the condenser. When little liquid remains in the distilling flask, the head temperature drops and no more liquid is obtained as distillate. A plot of temperature (in the distillation head) versus volume of distillate for the distillation of cyclohexane (bp 81°C) is shown in Figure 1G-3.

It is common to distill a mixture of liquids, such as cyclohexane and toluene. Just as for pure cyclohexane, the solution of cyclohexane and toluene boils when the vapor

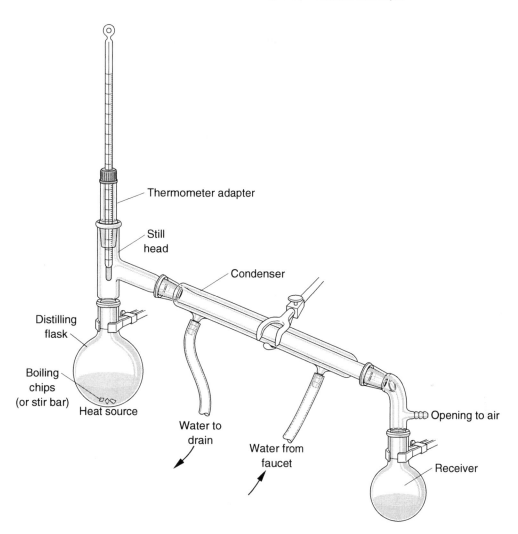

Figure 1G-1   Simple distillation apparatus

pressure above the solution (P_{tot}) is equal to the atmospheric pressure (P_{atm}). The contributions of each component to the total pressure are called partial pressures, $P_{cyclohexane}$ and $P_{toluene}$. Dalton's Law of Partial Pressures states that the partial pressures are additive. A solution will boil when $P_{atm} = P_{tot}$; that is, at the boiling point:

$$P_{atm} = P_{tot} = P_{cyclohexane} + P_{toluene} \qquad (1.1)$$

Raoult's Law states that there is a simple proportionality between solvent mol fraction (X) and its partial pressure (P) at a given temperature. For mixtures of liquids that obey Raoult's Law, the partial pressure of each of the components of a solution is equal to the product of the vapor pressure of the pure component ($P°$) at a particular temperature and the mol fraction (X) of the component. Mol fraction is equal to the number of moles of a component divided by the total number of moles of all components.

Raoult's Law:

$$\text{partial pressure of cyclohexane} = P_{cyclohexane} = P°_{cyclohexane} X_{cyclohexane} \qquad (1.2)$$

$$\text{partial pressure of toluene} = P_{toluene} = P°_{toluene} X_{toluene} \qquad (1.3)$$

Figure 1G-2

Vapor pressure-
temperature diagram

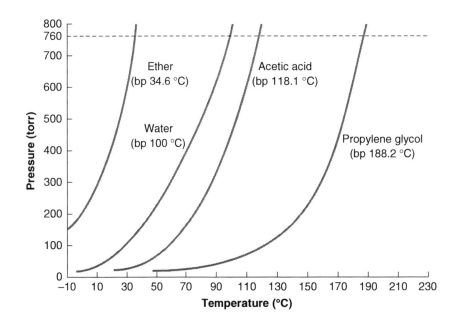

Figure 1G-3

Simple distillation of
30 mL of cyclohexane

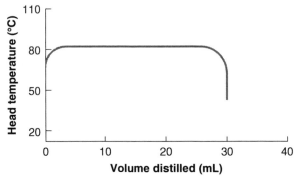

Equation (1.1) may be rewritten as the commonly used expression of Raoult's Law:

(1.4) $P_{tot} = P°_{cyclohexane} X_{cyclohexane} + P°_{toluene} X_{toluene}$

In Equation (1.4), the total vapor pressure of the solution is equal to the product of the vapor pressure of pure cyclohexane at a particular temperature and the mol fraction of cyclohexane plus the product of the vapor pressure of pure toluene at the same temperature and its mol fraction.

Example 1: Calculate the vapor pressure of a solution of 0.600 mol fraction of toluene and 0.400 mol fraction of cyclohexane at 32°C and determine whether the solution will boil. The vapor pressure of pure cyclohexane is 125 torr and the vapor pressure of pure toluene is 40.2 torr at 32°C.

Solution: Calculate the total vapor pressure using Equation (1.4).

$$P_{tot} = P°_{cyclohexane} X_{cyclohexane} + P°_{toluene} X_{toluene}$$

$$= (125 \text{ torr})(0.400) + (40.2 \text{ torr})(0.600)$$

$$= 50.0 \text{ torr} + 24.1 \text{ torr}$$

$$= 74.1 \text{ torr}$$

Since the total vapor pressure is below 760 torr, the solution will not boil at 32°C.

Example 2: Calculate the vapor pressure of pure toluene in a solution of 0.500 mol fraction of toluene and cyclohexane where the solution begins to boil (94°C) at sea level (760 torr). The vapor pressure (see CRC) of cyclohexane is 1100 torr at 94°C.

Solution: Use Equation (1.4), to solve for the vapor pressure of pure toluene.

$$P_{atm} = P_{tot} = P°_{cyclohexane}X_{cyclohexane} + P°_{toluene}X_{toluene}$$

$$760 \text{ torr} = (1100 \text{ torr})(0.500) + P°_{toluene}(0.500)$$

$$P°_{toluene} = (760 - 550)/0.500 \text{ torr} = 420 \text{ torr}$$

The solution in Example 2 starts to boil at a temperature that lies between the boiling points of the two components. This is represented graphically for binary mixtures of cyclohexane and toluene in Figure 1G-4. The composition of the initial distillate formed in Example 2 can be determined from a plot of temperature versus composition. The vertical axis on the left is pure toluene and the axis on the right is pure cyclohexane. To find the composition of the initial distillate for the solution in Example 2, draw a vertical line from the mol fraction of the solution (0.50 mol fraction) until it intersects the liquid curve at point A. From A, draw a horizontal line (a tie line) to intersect the vapor curve at point B. Then, draw a perpendicular from B to the baseline. This gives the approximate composition of the first drops of distillate (about 0.75 mol fraction of cyclohexane) for the distillation of a solution that is 0.50 mol fraction in each component. The tie line A-B intersects the liquid and vapor curves and shows the boiling point of the mixture.

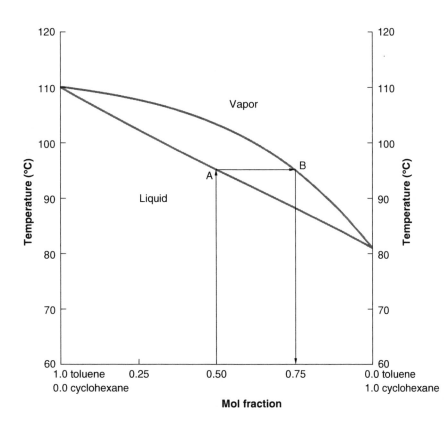

Figure 1G-4

Temperature-composition diagram for the toluene-cyclohexane system

The experimentally determined composition of the vapor above a solution is not the same as the composition of the solution. The vapor is always richer in the more volatile component than the solution. A toluene/cyclohexane solution having a mol fraction of 0.50 of cyclohexane has a vapor composition that is about 0.75 mol fraction cyclohexane.

The boiling point of the distillate changes during the distillation as diagrammed in Figure 1G-5. Early in the distillation, the boiling point of the distillate is closer to that of cyclohexane and the composition of the distillate is closer to that of cyclohexane. Examination of the temperature-composition diagram indicates that the initial distillate is about 75% cyclohexane. As the distillation progresses, the composition of the distillate changes. The distillate becomes richer in toluene and the boiling point of the distillate increases. Pure cyclohexane and toluene cannot be obtained by this method, but simple distillation will work to give pure compounds if the difference in boiling points is at least 100°C.

Microscale

Microscale Apparatus for Simple Distillation and Assembly

Examples of typical microscale distillation equipment are shown in Figure 1G-6. Assemble as shown in the inset. In Apparatus A, a Hickman still is employed. This is a glass tube that has a collar to catch condensed distillate as it flows from the top of the still downward toward the distilling flask. Some Hickman stills have a small exit port near the collar that is opened to allow convenient removal of distillate at appropriate intervals. Apparatus B is similar to Apparatus A except that a condenser is placed above the Hickman still. This apparatus is used for distilling solutions of volatile liquids (bp < 100°C), which require a cold condenser to trap and condense the vapors. The condensed liquid falls from the condenser back into the distilling vial. A drying tube may be attached to the top of the condenser, if necessary, to keep moisture away from the distillate. Unless directed otherwise, do not grease joints.

Several methods of heating are used for microscale distillation. A metal heating block on a hot plate is the most popular heating method. A hot sand bath, using heat from a hot plate, is another option. Hot water or steam baths can be used for those distillations where the boiling point of the distillate is below 100°C.

Microscale

How to Do a Simple Microscale Distillation

Place a hot plate stirrer on the bench if you are using a spin vane or a spin bar or a hot plate if using boiling chips. Place a sand bath or heat block on the hot plate. Add a spin

Figure 1G-5

Distillate temperature vs. volume distilled

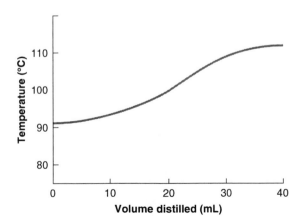

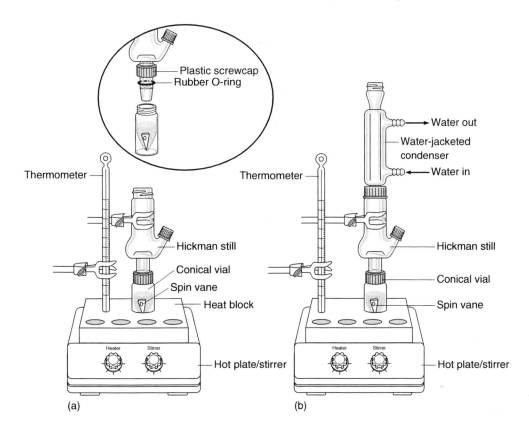

Figure 1G-6   Microscale distillation apparatus and assembly of glassware

vane or a boiling chip to a 3-mL or 5-mL conical vial. Use a 3-mL conical vial for volumes of 0.5–2.0 mL and a 5-mL conical vial for volumes of 2.0–3.5 mL. Clamp the distilling vial to a ring stand. Add the liquid or solution to be distilled to the vial. The vial should not be more than two-thirds full. Attach a Hickman still to the top of the vial and tighten the screwcap. Use an O-ring to seal the joint. If desired, a condenser may be used on top of the Hickman still. Use a water condenser for volatile liquids or an air condenser for high-boiling liquids (bp > 150°C). Fit a thermometer into the top of the apparatus using a clamp. Leave the system open to the outside atmosphere. **Never heat a totally closed system.** Position the thermometer inside the Hickman still so that the thermometer bulb reaches down into the neck of the vial but does not touch the sides of the vial. A typical apparatus is shown in Figure 1G-7.

   Turn on the heat source. If using a sand bath, the temperature of the sand bath should be about 20°C higher than the boiling point of the liquid or the boiling point of the lowest boiling component of a solution before distillation will occur. Turn up the heat until the liquid begins to boil. Drops will appear on the thermometer bulb and the temperature of the thermometer inside the apparatus will increase. Liquid will collect in the collar of the Hickman still. Discard the first few drops of distillate. Using a Pasteur pipet, transfer condensed liquid at intervals from the collar to a clean vial. Record the temperature and volume of each aliquot. The observed boiling temperature will be lower than the reported boiling point of the liquid. This is because the small volumes of liquid being distilled do not thoroughly bathe the thermometer bulb. An accurate boiling point can be obtained by performing a boiling point or micro boiling point determination.

Figure 1G-7

Simple microscale distillation apparatus

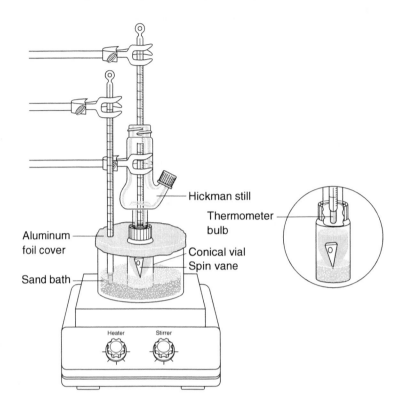

Never heat the vial or flask to dryness since explosions can occur and because flasks containing decomposed organic matter are difficult to clean. When only a few drops of liquid remain in the vial, turn off the hot plate and allow the apparatus to cool. Loosen the caps and raise the apparatus by loosening the clamp and moving it up an inch or two and retightening it. Cap and label all sample vials; store in your locker or in a refrigerator until the distillate fractions can be analyzed. Cover with parafilm also, if directed.

Microscale

Important Tips Concerning Microscale Distillation

1. **Never heat a system that is totally closed from the outside atmosphere because an explosion is very likely to occur as pressure builds up.**
2. **Never heat a system to dryness because of possible explosion.**
3. Do not fill the distillation vial more than two-thirds full. Overfilling may cause the liquid in the vial to bump and contaminate the distillate.
4. Add boiling chips or a spin vane to reduce bumping. Never add a boiling chip to a solution that is already boiling. Doing so will cause the liquid to bump violently.
5. Place the thermometer properly in the neck of the microscale vial when using a Hickman still. For other distilling heads, place the bulb of the thermometer below the exit for the condenser. Remember that the observed thermometer reading in a microscale distillation might be lower than the reported boiling point because very small amounts are being distilled.
6. Control the rate of heating carefully so that the distillation vial does not become overheated. An overheated distilling vial may lead to bumping.
7. Be very careful when connecting tubing to condensers. Do not use excessive force. Use a lubricant, such as water or glycerine, or try another section of tubing

if there is a problem. Be sure that the **correct diameter tubing** is being used. Attach the tubing **before** connecting the condenser to the vial. Tubing can be fastened using wire.

8.   Handle a hot plate near the base, rather than at the top. The top may be hot!

Miniscale Apparatus for Simple Distillation

Miniscale

Refer to the typical miniscale distillation setup in Figure 1G-8. Important pieces are the Variac, heating mantle, distilling flask, stir bar or boiling chips, still head, thermometer, condenser, bent adapter, and receiving flask.

How to Do a Simple Miniscale Distillation

Assemble the apparatus from the bottom up. Choose the correct size heating mantle. Connect the electrical cords from the mantle to the Variac and from the Variac to the electrical outlet. Do not turn on the Variac until setup is complete. Clamp the distilling flask to a ring stand, insert the stir bar or boiling chips, and add the distilling head and thermometer. Position the bulb of the thermometer below the opening in the still head leading to the condenser. Do not grease standard-taper joints except when alkali is used and then grease joints only lightly.

Attach tubing to the condenser (one for water in and the other for water out) and clamp the condenser to a second ring stand. Tighten the clamp enough to hold the condenser, but loosely enough that the condenser can slide onto the standard-taper joint of the

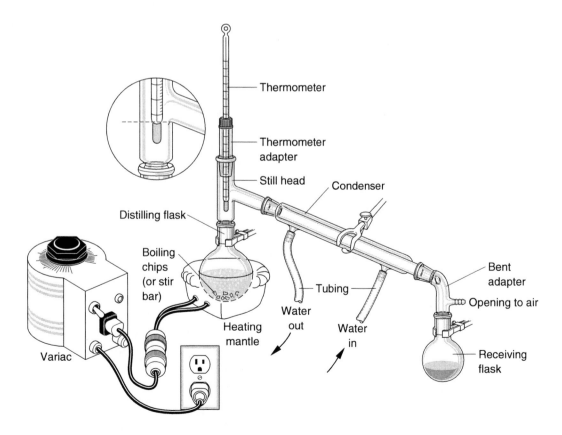

Figure 1G-8   Apparatus for simple miniscale distillation

still head. Attach a bent adapter to the condenser and place a receiving vessel beneath the adapter to collect the distillate. Use a third ring stand, if necessary, to position and clamp the receiving vessel. When all parts are connected, remove the distilling head and add the solution to be distilled. Replace the still head and reconnect the condenser. (See Figure 1G-8.) Alternatively, place the liquid to be distilled in the distilling flask when attaching the flask to the ring stand initially. Check to make sure that all joints are tightly fitted and that there are no leaks. If the liquid is high boiling (bp > 125°C), insulate the distilling flask and still head using aluminum foil or glass wool. Do not wrap the condenser.

Turn on the stirrer if a spin bar is being used. Turn the Variac to a low setting (~30) and then increase the setting as necessary to bring the liquid to boiling. Turn on the water in the condenser before the distillate begins to come over through the condenser. Discard the first few drops of distillate as they often contain low-boiling impurities or water. Adjust the Variac so that the rate of distillation is 1 to 2 drops per second.

If a mixture of liquids is being distilled, it will be necessary to turn up the setting of the Variac during the distillation. This may have to be done more than once depending on the boiling points of the components of the mixture. Divide the distillate, if desired, into several fractions by periodically changing receiving vessels. Collect the distillate at a given temperature range and change receiving vessels when the temperature changes. (Correct boiling points for atmospheric pressure.) The purest liquid is that which is distilled at constant temperature at the boiling point of the liquid. Label all receiving vessels and record the boiling range of each. Record the volumes or weights of each fraction. Cover each vessel until such time as the fractions can be analyzed.

As the liquid in the distilling flask reaches a small volume, turn off the Variac and stop the distillation. Never heat a distilling flask to dryness! There may be danger of explosion in certain cases. Also, distilling flasks that have been heated to dryness are frequently difficult to clean. Disassemble the cooled equipment as soon as possible in the order opposite to which it was assembled and then wash it and set aside to dry.

Miniscale

Important Tips Concerning Miniscale Distillation

1. **Never heat a system that is totally closed from the outside atmosphere because an explosion may occur due to pressure buildup.**
2. **Never heat a system to dryness because of possible explosion.**
3. Use a calibrated thermometer so that accurate temperature readings can be obtained.
4. Do not fill the distilling flask more than two-thirds full. Overfilling causes bumping, which will contaminate the distillate.
5. Control the heating rate carefully to avoid overheating the distilling flask. An overheated flask may cause bumping and may give an observed boiling point that is too high due to superheating of the solution.
6. Add boiling chips or a stir bar to the flask prior to distillation to minimize bumping. Never add boiling chips to a solution that is already boiling. Doing so causes violent bumping.
7. Turn up the heat gradually during distillation. A certain amount of heat is necessary to start the distillation. After some of the liquid has distilled, turn up the heat to ensure a steady flow of condensate, because the boiling point of distillate may increase, particularly in the case of mixtures.
8. When distilling a high-boiling component, wrap the distilling flask and still head with aluminum foil or glass wool for insulation.
9. Compounds having high boiling points (> 150°C) do not require a flow of cold water through the condenser.

Introduction to Reflux

Reflux is continual boiling of a solution in a vial or flask where the solvent is continually returned to the reaction vessel from a condenser atop the vial or flask. The condenser is usually water cooled and often a drying tube is connected to the top of the condenser to keep moisture away from the solution.

Reflux is one of the most common techniques for carrying out organic reactions. Using this technique it is possible to heat a reaction mixture at the boiling point of the solvent without losing the solvent through evaporation. Molecules of liquid are vaporized due to heating the vial or flask. As they escape from the flask, they encounter the cooling effect of the condenser and they condense to be returned to the flask. Reactions can be heated for several hours, days, or even weeks as long as water pressure is maintained to keep cool water flowing through the condenser. In this text, reflux times are 75 minutes or less.

Reaction rates of most organic reactions are faster at higher temperature. A rough rule of thumb is that the reaction rate doubles for every 10°C rise in the reaction temperature. Raising the reaction temperature has a dramatic effect on reaction rates of reactions that have high activation energies. The effect is less dramatic for reactions that have low activation barriers. If it takes an hour to accomplish a reaction in boiling diethyl ether, the reaction should take only about 5–10 minutes in boiling tetrahydrofuran, a cyclic ether with a boiling point 30°C higher than diethyl ether. Reflux setups are shown in Figure 1G-9.

How to Do a Microscale Reaction with Reflux   **Microscale**

Obtain a hot plate/stirrer if using a spin vane or a hot plate if using boiling chips. Place a sand bath or heat block on the hot plate. Attach a vial containing a boiling chip or spin vane to a clamp connected to a ring stand. Place the solution to be refluxed in the

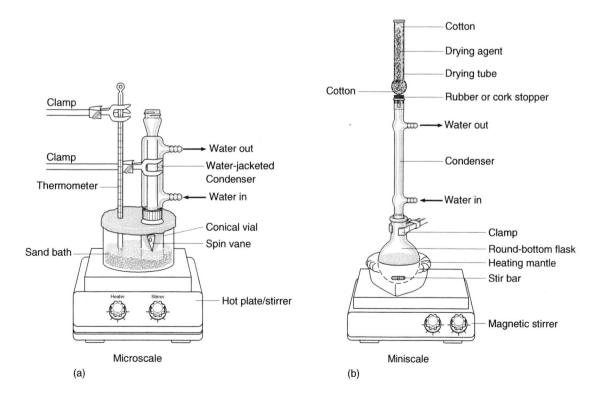

Figure 1G-9 Microscale and miniscale reflux equipment

vial. The vial should not be more than two-thirds full. If a sand bath is used, push the vial down into the sand so that it is partially immersed in the sand, guaranteeing a good transfer of heat from the sand to the vial. Connect tubing to the condenser. Attach the condenser with rubber o-ring and plastic cap to the vial as shown in Figure 1G-9. If moisture must be excluded from the reaction, attach a calcium chloride drying tube to the top of the condenser. Add a wad of cotton to the tube, then the drying agent and a second wad of cotton to contain the drying agent. Turn on the water to the condenser. Turn on the hot plate (and stirrer, if applicable) and adjust to a setting that assures vapors from the solution going up into the condenser and condensing to return to the solution. Vapors should not escape from the top of the condenser. Reduce the heat setting if vapors condense more than one-third up into the condenser. Reflux the solution for the designated time. Check the apparatus periodically. When finished, turn off the hot plate, but allow stirring to continue to avoid bumping. When at room temperature, turn off the water and disassemble the apparatus. Wash all glassware.

Miniscale

How to Do a Miniscale Reaction with Reflux

Attach a round-bottom flask containing a boiling chip or stir bar to a clamp connected to a ring stand. Place the solution to be refluxed in the flask. Fill the flask no more than two-thirds full. Fit a heating mantle of the proper size to the flask and connect to a Variac. Connect the Variac to the outlet. Do not turn on the Variac until setup is complete. Attach a water condenser, with hoses already connected, to the flask. Wire the hoses, if directed by your instructor. If necessary, attach a calcium chloride drying tube to the top of the condenser. Add a wad of cotton to the tube, then the drying agent and a second wad of cotton to contain the drying agent. Do not grease standard-taper joints unless the solution is basic. Even then, apply only a thin film of grease. Start water flowing through the condenser and turn on the Variac. Adjust to a setting that sends solvent vapors up into the condenser and condensing liquid back into the solution. Vapors should not escape from the top of the condenser. Reduce the heat setting if vapors condense more than one-third up into the condenser. Reflux the solution for the designated time. Check the apparatus periodically. When finished, turn off the Variac, but allow stirring to continue to avoid bumping. When at room temperature, turn off the water and disassemble the apparatus. Wash all glassware.

Important Tips on Reflux

1. Always clamp the vial or flask to a ring stand.
2. Connect tubing to the condenser prior to assembling the reflux apparatus.
3. Add a boiling chip, spin vane, or spin bar.
4. Do not fill the distillation vial or flask over two-thirds full.
5. Apply enough heat to achieve reflux, but not excessive heat. Often the vapors can be seen condensing in the condenser. Condensation should occur near the bottom of the condenser.
6. Be sure to turn on the water to the condenser before starting to heat.
7. Check the apparatus periodically during reflux to be sure that solvent vapors are not escaping and that the proper amount of heat is being applied.
8. Recover the spin bar or spin vane as soon as possible after reflux as these are easily lost down the drain.

Evaporation of Solvents

Isolating a solid from solution often requires evaporation of the solvent. The microscale evaporation setups in Figure 1G-10(a), (b) or (c) can be used for evaporation of a volatile solvent. Solvent can be driven off under the hood with a stream of air or nitrogen or otherwise drawn off with a source of vacuum, such as a water aspirator. Miniscale evaporation can be done in a similar manner as shown in Figure 1G-10(b) or (c). For the apparatus in Figure 1G-10(c), solvent is evaporated from a suction flask under vacuum. This setup is sometimes also used in microscale procedures. In each setup, boiling chips or a spin vane or stir bar should be used to prevent bumping.

Exercise G.1: Distilling a Cyclohexane/Toluene Mixture

Pipet 1.25 mL each of cyclohexane and toluene into a 5-mL conical vial that contains a spin vane or boiling chip. Connect a Hickman still to the vial and assemble the apparatus as shown in Figure 1G-7. Position a thermometer in the thermometer adapter so that the thermometer is centered in the middle of the joint of the Hickman still. Turn on the heat source and slowly raise the temperature until vapors can be seen in the still. These vapors will recondense in the collar of the Hickman still. Use a pipet, calibrated in 0.1-mL divisions, to withdraw the liquid collected in the collar and to estimate the volume of distillate recovered. Record the temperature at the time that the aliquot was taken. Collect distillate at intervals from the lip of the Hickman still. Continue the distillation until there is only about 0.5 mL of liquid remaining in the conical vial. Remove the heat source and let the apparatus cool to room temperature. Place all organic liquids in an appropriately labeled container. Correct the boiling points to standard pressure. Estimate and record the temperature ranges at which fractions were collected and estimate the volumes of distillate collected at each temperature. Graph the corrected boiling temperature versus volume (mL) of distillate.

Microscale

Safety First!

Always wear eye protection in the laboratory.

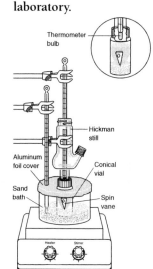

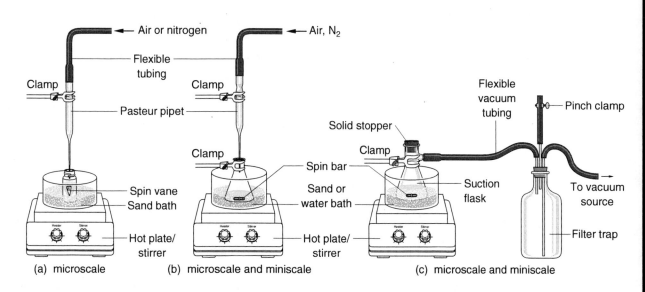

Figure 1G-10   Setups for evaporation of volatile solvents (in hood)

Miniscale

Exercise G.2: Distilling a Mixture of Cyclohexane and Toluene

Safety First!

Always wear eye protection in the laboratory.

Lay out all of the glassware needed to perform a simple distillation. Make certain that each piece of glassware is clean, dry, and free of star cracks. Refer to Figure 1G-8 for an illustration of the apparatus for simple miniscale distillation.

Pipet 10.0 mL each of cyclohexane and toluene into a 50-mL round-bottom flask that contains a spin bar or boiling chip. Assemble the apparatus for simple distillation as shown in Figure 1G-8. Position the bulb of the thermometer below the neck of the distilling head. Be certain that the bent adapter fits well into the neck of a graduated cylinder to minimize evaporation of the distillate. Gently turn on the water to the condenser. Turn on the Variac and heat the solution until vapors reach the thermometer bulb. Increase the rate of heating. Discard the first few drops of distillate, which may contain water or volatile impurities. Collect distillate in the receiver at the rate of 1–2 drops per second. Record the temperature versus volume (mL) of distillate during the entire distillation. Take readings after every 1–2 mL, or more frequently if the temperature is changing rapidly. As the distillation proceeds, cyclohexane will be depleted and the pot will become enriched in toluene. It may be necessary to increase the heat to continue the distillation at a suitable rate. Stop the distillation when 1–2 mL remains in the pot. Remove the heat source and let the apparatus cool to room temperature. Disassemble the distillation apparatus. Place all organic liquids in an appropriately labeled container. Wash and dry all glassware. Correct the boiling points to standard pressure. Estimate and record the temperature ranges at which fractions were collected and estimate the volumes of distillate collected at each temperature. Graph the corrected boiling temperature versus volume (mL) of distillate.

Questions

1. What is the relationship between volatility and the vapor pressure of a solvent?

2. Explain what happens to the vapor pressure of a liquid as temperature increases. Are temperature and vapor pressure directly proportional? If not, explain the relationship by drawing a graph.

3. Explain Dalton's Law of Partial Pressures. Is Dalton's law dependent upon ideal behavior? Explain.

4. Why is it preferable to allow cold water to enter at the bottom of a condenser and exit at the top rather than vice versa?

5. Explain the difference between the vapor pressure of a pure solvent ($P^{\circ}_{solvent}$) and its partial pressure ($P_{solvent}$).

6. Can the vapor pressure of a liquid be greater than 1 atm? Explain.

7. What possible hazard might occur if a distillation vessel is heated all the way to dryness?

8. Refer to Figure 1G-4. Predict the boiling point of the initial drops of distillate from the distillation of a mixture that contains 0.80 mol fraction of toluene and 0.20 mol fraction of cyclohexane.

9. Is it proper procedure to add the boiling chips down through the condenser once a solution has started to reflux? What is expected to happen if this procedure is followed?

10. A certain reaction requires 80 minutes to reach completion in refluxing diethyl ether (bp 35°C). Estimate the reflux time required if the reaction is run in tetrahydrofuran (bp 65°C).

Technique H: Fractional Distillation and Steam Distillation

Introduction to Fractional Distillation

Fractional distillation improves separation of components of a mixture beyond that which is possible in a simple distillation. Simple distillation is generally unsatisfactory unless the components have vastly different boiling points (about a 100°C difference). A mixture of cyclohexane and toluene cannot be separated into pure cyclohexane and pure toluene by simple distillation because the boiling points of these compounds are too close together. Better separation can be achieved by fractional distillation. The key to an efficient fractional distillation is the number of vaporization-condensation cycles provided by the apparatus. Each cycle is equivalent to a separate simple distillation. A simple distillation gives a single vaporization-condensation cycle. (Refer to Figure 1G-4.) To understand the greater efficiency of fractional distillation, refer to the temperature-composition diagram (Figure 1H-1) for fractional distillation of a solution containing 0.50 mol fraction each of toluene and cyclohexane.

The diagram shows the expected initial boiling point and vapor composition for a fractional distillation apparatus that gives two vaporization-condensation cycles. The two-step sequence can be traced by drawing a vertical line shown from the 0.50-mol fraction mark on the x axis up to point A on the liquid curve. Connecting the tie line A-B gives the vapor composition for the first cycle at point B. In a simple distillation, the distillate will contain 0.75 mol fraction of cyclohexane and boil at 94°C. However, in the fractional distillation, the vapor recondenses (B to point C). The second tie line C-D gives the vapor composition at point D (from the intersection of a vertical line drawn from D to the x axis) after the second vaporization-condensation cycle. For this distillation, the initial distillate should contain 0.87 mol fraction of cyclohexane and boil at 86°C. The boiling point and composition of the initial distillate from a three-cycle distillation of a mixture of cyclohexane and toluene will boil at 84°C and contain 0.97 mol fraction of cyclohexane. Most fractional distillations carried out in the first-year organic laboratory achieve two- or three-cycle efficiency. Special columns, called spinning band columns, are required to obtain greater efficiency. Fractional distillation requires the same equipment as simple distillation, plus one extra piece of glassware, called a fractionating column, as shown in Figure 1H-2.

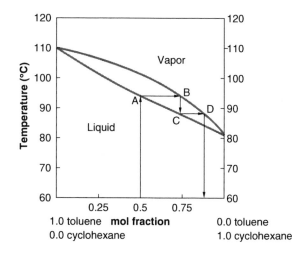

Figure 1H-1

Temperature-composition diagram for the toluene-cyclohexane system

Organic Chemistry Laboratory CHM 375 & CHM 376

Figure 1H-2

Miniscale fractional distillation setup

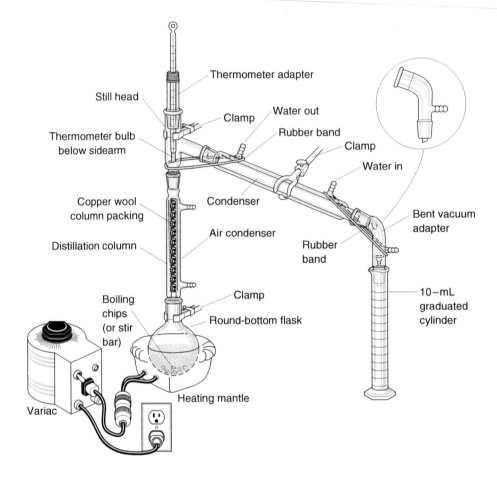

The fractionating column fits directly into the distilling flask. The most common fractionating columns are glass columns, such as a Vigreux column, that are specially designed to contain a high surface area, affording a greater equilibration of the vapor above the distilling flask. Alternatives are packed glass tubes containing metal sponge, glass helices, or glass beads. Equilibration differentiates between more-volatile and less-volatile molecules. The effect is much the same as doing multiple simple distillations back to back, but more efficiently. Examples of fractionating columns and packing materials are shown in Figure 1H-3.

The metal or glass packing in the fractionating columns serves to provide more surface area for vapor to condense. A drawback to the increased area is that there is more "hold-up" of the vapor. This can be a serious problem in columns that are packed with glass beads or glass helices. Liquid that is expected to distill can become "lost" in the fractionating column. Columns that have significant hold-up should be used only for distilling large volumes of liquid. A comparison of hold-up and efficiencies of different types of columns is shown in Table 1H-1.

Vigreux columns work well in miniscale distillation because of small hold-up. However, unless a mixture of liquids is used that has at least a 60°C difference in boiling points, only partial separation can be achieved. A Vigreux column or a column using one of the packings listed in Table 1H-1 can be used for miniscale fractional distillation as described later in Exercise H.2.

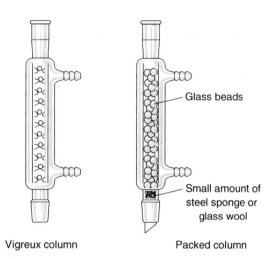

Vigreux column   Packed column

— Glass beads

— Small amount of
  steel sponge or
  glass wool

Figure 1H-3

Fractional distillation
columns

Table 1H-1   Properties of Fractionating Columns Used for
Miniscale Distillation

Column packing	Distillation cycles	Boiling point difference required	Hold-up
Metal sponge	2	70	moderate
Vigreux (no packing)	2	60	small
Glass beads	3	55	moderate
Glass helices	5	35	moderate

How to Do a Miniscale Fractional Distillation

Miniscale

Glassware used in miniscale fractional distillation is shown in Figure 1H-2 on page 66.
Clamp the distilling flask to a ring stand and add a stir bar or boiling chips and the liquid
to be distilled. Attach the fractionating column. Place the still head and thermometer on
top of the column. Position the bulb of the thermometer adjacent to the arm of the still
head leading to the condenser. Do not grease standard-taper joints except when alkali is
used and then grease joints very lightly upon assembling the apparatus. Attach tubing to
the condenser (bottom for water coming in and top for water going out) and clamp the
condenser to a second ring stand. Tighten the clamp enough to hold the condenser, but
loosely enough that the condenser can slide onto the standard-taper joint of the still head.
Attach a bent adapter to the condenser and place a receiving flask beneath the adapter to
collect the distillate. Turn on the stirrer if a spin bar is being used. Turn on the Variac to a
low setting (~30) and increase the setting as necessary to bring the liquid to boiling.
High-boiling liquids may require insulation of the glass parts that are being heated. Wrap
the distilling flask, fractionating column, and still head with aluminum foil.

   Turn on water to the condenser unless the liquid being distilled is high boiling
(>150°C), in which case it is not necessary to use a water-cooled condenser. The temperature of the thermometer in the still head will remain at room temperature until the
first vapors of liquid meet the thermometer bulb. It is usually possible to observe a ring
of condensate advancing up the fractionating column. The temperature rises rapidly as
the distillate reaches the boiling point of the most volatile component. The temperature
increases gradually as the lower boiling component distills away and some of the higher
boiling component begins to distill.

When a mixture of liquids is being distilled, it will be necessary to turn up the setting of the Variac during the distillation. This may have to be done more than once depending on the boiling points of the components of the mixture. A good rate of distillation is at least 1 to 2 drops per second. An acceptable rate depends on the amount of liquid to be distilled.

When distilling a mixture, the distillate may be divided into several fractions by periodically changing receiving vessels. Collect the distillate at a given temperature and change receiving vessels when the temperature changes.

When the liquid in the distilling flask reaches 1–2 mL, turn off the Variac to stop the distillation, but continue stirring. Do not heat to dryness. When the apparatus is cool, turn off the water and disassemble the equipment in the order opposite to which it was assembled. Record the boiling range and volumes or weights of each fraction. Cap each vessel to preserve the samples for analysis. After the apparatus has cooled, wash the glassware and allow to dry.

Miniscale

Practical Tips about Miniscale Fractional Distillation

The tips given in Technique G for simple distillation also apply to fractional distillation. Additional points of emphasis are given here.

1. Be very careful when assembling the fractional distillation apparatus. The apparatus is tall and high clearance is necessary on the lab bench. Use clamps and ring stands to support the apparatus, not books or notebooks. The apparatus should be stable upon assembly and should not teeter.
2. Don't lay the thermometer down near the edge of the bench. It is very common for thermometers to break during assembly and disassembly of fractional distillation equipment.
3. Be prepared to apply more heat for fractional distillation than for simple distillation of a comparable solution. The vapors of distillate must travel a greater vertical distance before reaching the condenser or still head. It is often useful to wrap the fractionating column with aluminum foil. It is easy to observe the effect of heating the distilling flask as the hot vapors begin to pass up through the fractionating column. Gently touch the outside of the column at various heights of the column. Alternatively, observe a ring of vapor that rises up through the fractionating column as the first vapors are pushed upward. Peel back a section of aluminum foil wrapping if necessary. Ultimately, the vapors come into contact with the thermometer bulb and the thermometer shows a rise in temperature.
4. Sometimes the temperature observed in the still head will decrease during distillation. This means that additional heat must be supplied and it might be a good time to change receiving vessels if multiple fractions are being collected.

Introduction to Steam Distillation

Many organic substances begin to decompose at temperatures above 230°C. In steam distillation, all volatile matter distills together with water at temperatures just below 100°C, thus avoiding high-temperature decomposition. Steam distillation is a useful method for isolating high-boiling liquids, known as oils, from other nonvolatile organic compounds, such as waxes, complex fats, proteins, and sugars.

The technique of steam distillation is based upon the principle that each component of immiscible liquid mixtures contributes to the total vapor pressure as if the other components were not there. Natural oils can be isolated readily by steam distillation. For example, if lemon grass oil and water are placed in a flask with water, and heat or steam is added, the distillate will contain water and volatile oils, mostly a water-insoluble substance called citral.

$$CH_3$$
$$|$$
$$(CH_3)_2CH=CHCH_2CH_2C=CHCHO$$

citral (mixture of cis and trans isomers)

A key feature concerning the theory of steam distillation is that the boiling point of the oily, aqueous distillate will never exceed the boiling point of water. This is because both water and the oily component each contribute to the total vapor pressure as if the other component were not present. The mixture boils when the combined vapor pressures of water and the oil equal the atmospheric pressure. The oil has a small, but significant vapor pressure at 100°C, so that the boiling point of the mixture will be just below the boiling point of water. This is true even though the boiling point of the oil is very high (citral, bp 229°C). Steam distillation allows separation and isolation of the oil at a low temperature (below 100°C) where citral will not decompose. Another advantage of steam distillation is that relatively small amounts of an oil can be successfully isolated. The technique is ideally suited for the isolation of oils from natural products.

Theory of Steam Distillation

Distilling a mixture of water and one or more immiscible organic liquids is called steam distillation. Raoult's Law does not apply to immiscible liquids because such liquids do not exhibit ideal behavior. Instead, each component of the mixture contributes its vapor pressure to the total pressure at a particular temperature as expressed in Equation (1.5):

$$P_{total} = P^°_{component\ 1} + P^°_{component\ 2} + P^°_{component\ n} + P^°_{water} \qquad (1.5)$$

When the total vapor pressure reaches atmospheric pressure, distillation occurs. $P^°$ values of each component are used in Equation (1.5) because each component exhibits a vapor pressure as if the other components were not there. Since the vapor pressure of water is 760 torr at 100°C, the presence of any organic material that contributes a vapor pressure will cause the boiling point to drop below 100°C. Nitrobenzene is a high-boiling liquid (bp 210–211°C). It has a vapor pressure of about 10 torr at 98°C where water has a vapor pressure of 750 torr. The mixture of nitrobenzene and water distills at 98°C, because the sum of their vapor pressures equals 760 torr at that temperature. Any organic liquid that is immiscible with water and exhibits even a small vapor pressure will steam distill at temperatures below 100°C. The mixture that passes through the condenser looks cloudy because it contains two immiscible phases. Generally, steam or boiling water is added to the distilling flask until the organic material has finished distilling. When this occurs, the distillate in the condenser will no longer appear cloudy because the distillate will contain only water.

The amount of water necessary to distill a given amount of organic material can be calculated using Equation (1.6). The mol fraction of organic substance is equal to the vapor pressure of the organic substance at the temperature of the distillate divided by the total pressure (atmospheric pressure).

$$\text{mol fraction of organic substance} = P^°_{organic\ substance}/P_{total} \qquad (1.6)$$

As an example, for the steam distillation of nitrobenzene, the mol fraction in the distillate is calculated using Equation (1.6).

$$\text{mol fraction of nitrobenzene} = P^°_{nitrobenzene}/P_{total} = 10\ torr/760\ torr = 1.32 \times 10^{-2}$$

$$\text{mol fraction of water} = 1 - 1.32 \times 10^{-2} = 0.987$$

This means that 1.32×10^{-2} mol of nitrobenzene will be distilled along with 0.987 mol of water. This translates to 17.8 g (= 18.0 g/mol × 0.987 mol) of water for every 1.63 g (= 1.32×10^{-2} mol × 123.11 g/mol) of nitrobenzene that will be distilled.

Miniscale

Safety First!

Always wear eye protection in the laboratory.

Hood!

Exercise H.1: Miniscale Fractional Distillation of a Mixture of Cyclohexane and Toluene

Lay out all of the glassware needed to perform fractional distillation. Make certain it is clean, dry, and free of star cracks. Pipet 10.0 mL each of cyclohexane and toluene into a 50-mL round-bottom flask that contains a spin bar or boiling chip. Alternatively, the instructor may assign different volumes. Assemble the apparatus as shown in Figure 1H-2. Position the bulb of the thermometer below the neck of the still head. Be certain that the bent adapter fits well into the neck of the receiving vessel (25-mL graduated cylinder) to minimize evaporation of the distillate. Gently turn on the water to the condenser. Turn on the heat source and heat the solution until vapors reach the thermometer bulb. This is a slow process. Insulating the column with aluminum foil will speed up the process. Increase the rate of heating so that distillate starts to appear in the receiver. Discard the first few drops of distillate, which may contain water or volatile impurities. Collect distillate in the receiver at the rate of 1 to 2 drops per second. Record the temperature versus volume (mL) of distillate during the entire distillation. Take readings after every mL or more frequently if the temperature is changing rapidly. As the distillation proceeds, cyclohexane will be depleted and the pot will become enriched in toluene. Increase the heat to maintain the distillation at a suitable rate. Stop distilling when about 0.5–1.0 mL remains in the pot. Remove the heat source and let the apparatus cool to room temperature. Turn off the flow of water and disassemble the apparatus. Place organic liquids in an appropriately labeled container. Wash all glassware and let dry. Correct the boiling points to standard pressure. Graph the corrected boiling temperature versus volume (mL) of distillate. Mark the temperature ranges at which pure cyclohexane and pure toluene were collected and estimate the volumes of pure cyclohexane and toluene. Use Raoult's Law to explain why the temperature changes as the distillation progresses. Calculate the initial mol fractions of cyclohexane and toluene in the mixture. Use Figure 1H-1 to determine the number of theoretical plates in the distillation.

Microscale

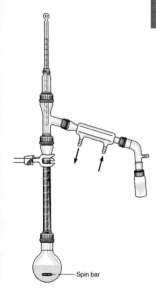

Spin bar

Exercise H.2: Microscale Fractional Distillation of Cyclohexane and Toluene

Place 3.0 mL cyclohexane and 3.0 mL toluene in a 10-mL round-bottom flask containing a spin bar. Prepare a fractional column by packing an air condenser with copper wool. Fit the fractional column to the flask. Place a connecting adapter on top of the column. Fit a thermometer adapter on top of the connecting adapter. Connect a water-jacketed condenser to the sidearm of the connecting adapter. Add a vacuum adapter to the water-jacketed condensor. A 5-mL conical vial will be used as a receiving flask. Place a thermometer into the thermometer adapter. The thermometer bulb must be just below the level of the sidearm of the connecting adapter.

Start the solution stirring. Turn on the heat to the aluminum heat block or sand bath and slowly heat. Discard the first few drops of distillate. Collect the next 3 drops of distillate in a clean vial labeled "fraction 1". Cap the vial tightly and set aside for further analysis. Connect the 5-mL conical vial to the vacuum adapter and collect the remaining distillate at a rate of 1-2 drops per second. Record the temperature and the estimated volume throughout the distillation. Distill until approximately 0.5 mL of liquid remains in the round-bottom flask. Then collect the last 3 drops of distillate in a clean vial labeled "fraction 2". Cap the vial tightly and set aside until ready to inject on the GC. Turn off the heat, let the system cool to room temperature, and disassemble the apparatus.

Correct boiling points for standard pressure. Graph the correcting boiling point temperature versus volume of distillate. Mark the temperature ranges at which pure cyclohexane and pure toluene were collected and estimate the volumes of pure cyclohexane and pure toluene. The composition of the initial and the final distillate can be analyzed, if desired, by refractometry (Technique E) or gas chromatography (Technique J).

Exercise H.3: Steam Distillation of Lemon Grass Oil

Miniscale

Safety First!

Always wear eye protection in the laboratory.

Hood!

Measure 1.0 mL of lemon grass oil (density = 0.87 g/mL) into a 50-mL round-bottom flask. Add 30 mL of water to the flask. Assemble the distillation apparatus for simple distillation with magnetic stirring (Figure 1G-8) or use a setup with a larger round-bottom flask that permits introduction of steam below the surface of the water. Ask your instructor to inspect your apparatus before proceeding. Heat (with stirring if using a simple distillation apparatus) and collect distillate in a 25-mL graduated cylinder until the distillate is no longer oily (after about 15–20 mL of distillate has been collected). Pour the distillate into a 125-mL separatory funnel. (See Technique I, Extraction and Drying.) Extract with two 10-mL portions of methylene chloride. Combine the methylene chloride solutions.

Dry the methylene chloride solution using about 1 g of anhydrous sodium sulfate. Swirl to be sure that no cloudiness remains in the methylene chloride solution. Gravity filter to remove the drying agent. (See Technique F, Recrystallization, Filtration, and Sublimation.) Distill the methylene chloride solution using simple distillation. (See Figure 1G-8.) Stop distilling when the volume in the distilling flask is about 2 mL. Transfer the distilled solvent to a bottle for recovered methylene chloride. Transfer the solution remaining in the distilling flask to a tared Erlenmeyer flask and evaporate the remaining solvent in the hood using a warm water bath or sand bath. There should be an oily residue remaining in the flask. Tilt the flask on its side for a few minutes to allow any remaining solvent vapors to escape. Weigh the flask and determine the amount of oil distilled. Measure the refractive index of the oil and compare the corrected value with the reported refractive index of citral (1.4876). What conclusion can you draw?

Questions

1. Explain how the following factors will affect the separation of cyclohexane from toluene and the overall efficiency of the separation:
   a. Heat is applied too rapidly.
   b. The distilling flask is more than two-thirds full.
   c. The distilling flask is less than one-tenth full.
   d. A very long fractionating column is used.
   e. No fractionating column is used.

2. How would the graph of temperature versus volume distilled appear for a perfect separation of methanol (bp 65.4°C) and toluene (bp 110°C) using an efficient fractionating column?

3. The efficiency of a fractional distillation is given as the number of cycles or theoretical plates. Traversing through steps A → D in Figure 1H-1 is equivalent to having completed two vaporization-condensation cycles or two theoretical plates.

Predict the temperature of the initial distillate for the solution used in Figure 1H-1 for a fractional distillation that is rated at four theoretical plates.

4. Define the following terms and explain how each affects the efficiency of a fractional distillation:

   a. theoretical plate.

   b. column hold-up.

5. A fractionating column filled with glass helices is rated at about 2 theoretical plates. How would the number of plates be affected if the column were used without the helices?

6. Suggest another possible way to obtain citral from lemon grass oil.

7. Does the boiling temperature ever exceed 100°C during steam distillation? Explain.

8. Can steam distillation of ethanol be done using a mixture of ethanol and water? Why or why not?

9. Give one or more reasons why microscale steam distillations may not give good results.

10. The vapor pressure of a water-insoluble organic substance is negligible at 100°C. Can this substance be purified by steam distillation? Explain.

11. Should steam distillation be considered as a method of isolation and purification of an organic liquid that has a vapor pressure of 760 torr at 46°C?

Technique I: Extraction and Drying

Introduction

Extraction is one of the most common methods of separating an organic product from a reaction mixture or a natural product from a plant. In liquid-liquid extraction, equilibrium concentrations of a solute are established between two immiscible solvents. Usually one of the solvents is water and the other is a moderately polar or nonpolar organic solvent, such as methylene chloride, petroleum ether, or diethyl ether. The concentration of solute in each solvent will depend upon the relative solubility of the solute in each of the immiscible solvents. The solute will be more concentrated in the solvent in which it is more soluble.

Extraction is commonly used to separate an organic product from a reaction mixture containing water-soluble impurities. The organic compound is preferentially drawn into the organic solvent in which it is more soluble. Other components, particularly if ionic or very polar, are preferentially drawn into the water. When the two layers are separated, the organic compound in the organic solvent has been freed from most of the water-soluble impurities.

In solid-liquid extraction, the theory is the same. Natural products are composed of a complex mixture of organic compounds. Isolating specific compounds from the solid involves repeated exposure of the solid to a solvent in which one or more components are soluble. These components dissolve in the solvent and are removed from the solid residue. Steeping a cup of tea is an example of a solid-liquid extraction. The hot water dissolves the flavoring and caffeine from the tea bag or tea leaves.

The terms "extraction" and "washing" imply slightly different processes, although the mechanics are the same. Extraction is the process of removing a compound of interest from a solution or a solid mixture. Brewing coffee is another example of a solid-liquid extraction: caffeine and other flavors are extracted from the bean by the hot water.

Washing, on the other hand, usually means removing impurities from the substance of interest. For example, an organic solution containing a neutral product may be washed with aqueous base to remove acidic impurities from the organic solution.

Theory

The organic solvent plays a pivotal role in liquid-liquid extraction. To serve as a good solvent for extraction of an organic compound, the solvent should:

* have high solubility for the organic compound.
* be immiscible with the other solvent (usually water).
* have a relatively low boiling point so as to be easily removed from the compound after extraction.
* be nontoxic, nonreactive, readily available, and inexpensive.

Typical solvents used for extraction are hexane, methylene chloride, diethyl ether, and ethyl acetate. The properties of these solvents are listed in Table 1I-1.

One of the most important properties of the solvent is its solubility for a particular organic compound. In an extraction, the organic compound is distributed between two different liquid phases: the organic solvent and water. The efficiency of extraction will depend upon the solubility of the compound in the two solvents. The ratio of solubilities is called the distribution coefficient (K_D). By usual convention, the distribution coefficient is equal to the solubility of a compound in an organic solvent divided by the solubility in water.

$$K_D = \frac{\text{solubility in organic solvent (g/100 mL)}}{\text{solubility in water (g/100 mL)}}$$

The units of solubility are typically given in grams of compound dissolved per 100 mL of solvent (written as g/100 mL). The magnitude of K_D gives an indication of the efficiency of extraction: the larger the value of K_D, the more efficient the extraction. If K_D is 1, equal amounts of the compound will dissolve in each of the phases. If K_D is much smaller than 1, the compound is more soluble in water than in the organic solvent.

If a compound has a low K_D for a given extraction, it is better to search for a different organic solvent in which the compound is more soluble in order to do a liquid-liquid extraction. If this is not feasible, doing multiple extractions can increase the amount of compound extracted.

Table 1I-1   Physical Properties of Organic Solvents Used in Extraction

Solvent	Solubility in H_2O	Boiling point (°C)	Density (g/mL)	Safety information
Methylene chloride CH_2Cl_2	Very slightly soluble	40	1.3255	Narcotic in high concentrations; suspected carcinogen
Diethyl ether $(CH_3CH_2)_2O$	Slightly soluble	35	0.7134	Very flammable; forms peroxides
Ethyl acetate $CH_3CO_2CH_2CH_3$	Fairly soluble	77	0.902	Flammable
Hexane $CH_3(CH_2)_4CH_3$	Insoluble	69	0.660	Narcotic in high concentrations

How to Do a Microscale Extraction

Place 1 to 2 mL of an aqueous solution containing the compound to be extracted in a 5-mL conical vial. Add 1 to 2 mL of an immiscible organic solvent. Cap and shake the vial to mix the layers thoroughly. Carefully vent by frequently loosening the cap. Repeat until the two phases are thoroughly mixed. Let the vial stand until the two layers have separated. Prepare a Pasteur filter pipet with a small cotton plug in the tip. The cotton plug helps to prevent volatile solvents from leaking out of the pipet. (See Figure 1F-4 in Technique F.)

In microscale extraction, the bottom layer is always removed from the extraction vessel first. (To see why, try to remove the top layer without getting any of the bottom layer.) This means that a different procedure is used, depending upon whether the organic phase is on the top or on the bottom.

If the organic solvent is more dense than water (such as methylene chloride, d = 1.3255), the organic solvent will be the bottom layer in the conical vial. Squeeze the bulb of the filter pipet to remove the air. Then place the tip of the filter pipet at the bottom of the conical vial. Very slowly release the bulb and draw up the organic layer into the pipet.

Figure 1I-1

Steps for the extraction of an aqueous solution using a solvent (CH_2Cl_2) that is more dense than water

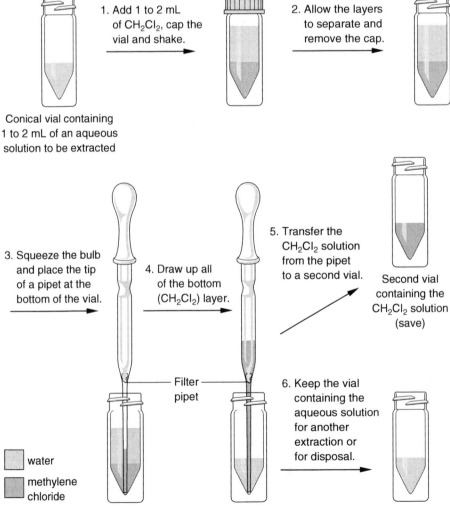

1. Add 1 to 2 mL of CH_2Cl_2, cap the vial and shake.

2. Allow the layers to separate and remove the cap.

Conical vial containing 1 to 2 mL of an aqueous solution to be extracted

3. Squeeze the bulb and place the tip of a pipet at the bottom of the vial.

4. Draw up all of the bottom (CH_2Cl_2) layer.

5. Transfer the CH_2Cl_2 solution from the pipet to a second vial.

Second vial containing the CH_2Cl_2 solution (save)

Filter pipet

6. Keep the vial containing the aqueous solution for another extraction or for disposal.

water

methylene chloride

Steps 1 to 5 can be repeated if two or more extractions are desired.

Be careful not to draw up any of the aqueous layer. Transfer the solution in the pipet to a clean conical vial or flask (see Figure 1I-1). Extract the aqueous layer remaining in the vial with additional portions of the organic solvent and combine the organic layers.

If the organic solvent is less dense than water (such as diethyl ether, d = 0.7134; hexane, d = 0.660; or ethyl acetate, d = 0.902), the organic solvent will be the top layer in the conical vial (see Figure 1I-2). Squeeze the bulb of the filter pipet to remove the air. Then place the tip of the filter pipet at the bottom of the conical vial. Very slowly release the bulb and draw up the aqueous layer into the pipet. The organic layer remains in the conical vial. Put the aqueous solution into a separate container. Transfer the organic layer to a clean vial or flask. Transfer the aqueous solution back to the original vial and add a second portion of organic solvent. Shake and vent. Separate the layers as before, but combine the organic layer with the organic layer from the first extraction. Repeat as necessary. Combine all organic layers.

An alternate procedure (not shown) can be used when the organic layer is less dense than water and the total volume of solution is 2 mL or less. In this procedure both of the solvents are drawn up into the pipet. Then the bottom layer is returned to the vial.

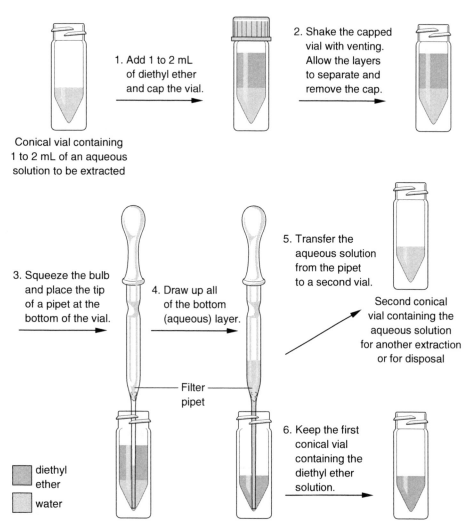

1. Add 1 to 2 mL of diethyl ether and cap the vial.

2. Shake the capped vial with venting. Allow the layers to separate and remove the cap.

Conical vial containing 1 to 2 mL of an aqueous solution to be extracted

Figure 1I-2

Steps for the extraction of a compound from an aqueous solution using an organic solvent (diethyl ether) that is less dense than water

3. Squeeze the bulb and place the tip of a pipet at the bottom of the vial.

4. Draw up all of the bottom (aqueous) layer.

5. Transfer the aqueous solution from the pipet to a second vial.

Second conical vial containing the aqueous solution for another extraction or for disposal

Filter pipet

6. Keep the first conical vial containing the diethyl ether solution.

diethyl ether

water

Steps 1 to 5 can be repeated if two or more extractions are desired.

Squeeze the bulb of the filter pipet to remove the air. Place the tip of the pipet at the bottom of the conical vial. Very slowly release the bulb and draw up all of the solution (both layers) into the filter pipet. Now gently squeeze the bulb to return the bottom aqueous layer to the conical vial. Put the organic layer into a clean conical vial or test tube. Repeat until the entire top layer is in a separate vial. Then add fresh solvent to the aqueous solution and repeat the extraction. Combine the organic layers.

How to Do a Miniscale Extraction

Attach an iron ring to a ring stand. Place a separatory funnel in the ring and an Erlenmeyer flask below the separatory funnel. Check to make sure that the stopcock is closed. Add approximately 1 mL of water to the separatory funnel to check for leaks. Using a stemmed funnel, pour the solution to be extracted into the separatory funnel. Add an approximately equal volume of the other solvent. Replace the stopper and give it a half-turn to seal in place. Cradle the separatory funnel in one hand while keeping the index finger on the top of the stopper. Gently invert the separatory funnel. Make sure that the stem of the separatory funnel is not directed at anyone. Slowly open the stopcock. A "whoosing" sound will be heard as the pressure is released. Close the stopcock. Shake the separatory funnel gently, then again open the stopcock. Repeat this process, but more vigorously, about five to six times until the two layers have thoroughly mixed. Vent one more time. Then invert the separatory funnel and place it in the ring to let the layers separate. Remove the stopper and set it on the lab bench. Allow the layers to clearly separate.

If the organic solvent is less dense than water, the organic solvent will be the top layer. Drain the lower aqueous layer into a clean flask. Pour the organic layer out of the top of the separatory funnel into a different clean flask. To do further extractions, return the aqueous layer to the separatory funnel. Add additional solvent and repeat the procedure. Combine the organic extracts.

If the organic solvent is more dense than water, the organic solvent will be the bottom layer. When the layers have separated, remove the stopcock and drain the lower organic layer into a clean flask. Add fresh solvent to the aqueous layer remaining in the separatory funnel and repeat the extraction procedure. Combine the organic extracts. This process is illustrated in Figure 1I-3.

Important Tips Concerning Extraction

1. **Never discard any layer until the experiment has been completed!** It is impossible to recover product from a layer that was discarded.
2. **Make certain that the phases are thoroughly mixed by vigorously shaking the container.** In order to be extracted from one solvent into another, the solvents must share as much surface area as possible to allow efficient transfer of the compound from one solvent to another.
3. Using one of these methods to determine which layer is the organic layer and which layer is the aqueous layer:
   a. Look up the densities of the solvents in the *Handbook of Chemistry and Physics* or the *Merck Index*; usually the more dense solvent will be on the bottom.
   b. Add 2–3 mL more water to the separatory funnel or 0.1–0.2 mL more water to the vial and see which layer grows; the layer that increases must be the aqueous layer.
   c. Put 1–2 drops from one of the layers onto a watch glass or in a small vial and add several drops of water. If two layers appear or if the mixture appears

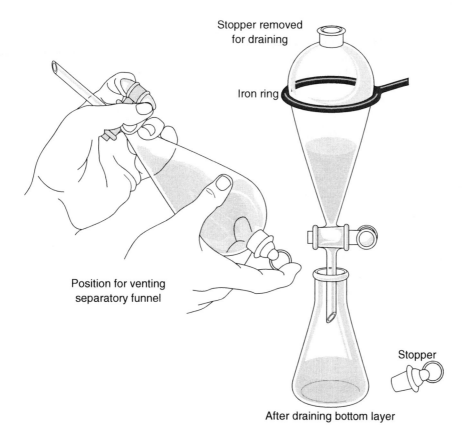

Figure 1I-3

Miniscale extraction
using separatory funnel

cloudy, the layer was organic. If the solution is clear and only one layer exists,
the layer was aqueous.

4. Vent frequently, especially with very volatile solvents such as diethyl ether or
   methylene chloride. Failure to do so could result in the top being blown off and the
   contents strewn all over the bench top. One way or the other, the pressure buildup
   will be alleviated! Do not vent the separatory funnel towards another person.

5. If there is only one layer in the conical vial or the separatory funnel and there
   should be two, perhaps the wrong layer was used. Try adding a little water and see
   what happens. If there is still only one layer, try adding some of the organic solvent. **Since nothing has been discarded** (Tip 1) there is no problem. Find the correct layer and repeat the extraction.

6. An emulsion is a suspension that prevents a sharp interface between the layers.
   Should an emulsion form, there are several things to try to break it up:
   a. Stir the mixture gently with a glass rod in the hopes of separating out the lay-
       ers, then let it stand undisturbed.
   b. Add a small portion of saturated sodium chloride solution (brine) or solid
       sodium chloride or other electrolyte to the solution. This increases the ionic
       strength of the aqueous layer, which may aid in the separation.
   c. For miniscale extractions using a separatory funnel, gravity filter the solution
       through filter paper. This should only be done after all else fails since filtering
       is slow and messy.

7. When considering the density of a solution, remember that the density of a dilute
   aqueous solution is approximately the same as the density of water.

Microscale Extraction

8. If it is difficult to keep the organic layer in the filter pipet, try drawing up and expelling several portions of the solvent before filtering the solution.
9. Never draw up liquid into the latex bulb! This contaminates both the liquid and the bulb.

Miniscale Extraction

10. If the liquid is not draining evenly from the separatory funnel, check to make certain that the stopper has been removed.
11. The proper way to hold a Teflon stopcock in a separatory funnel is to attach the Teflon washer first, then the rubber ring, then the nut.
12. To test for leaks, add a little water to the empty separatory funnel and examine the area around the stopcock for signs of leakage.
13. A Teflon stopcock should not be greased. A glass stopcock must be lightly greased to prevent leaking. Be sure that no grease gets in the opening of the stopcock. Glass stoppers should not be greased.

Drying and Drying Agents

During extraction, the organic layer becomes saturated with water. A drying agent must be used to remove water from the organic solvent. Drying agents are anhydrous salts that are used to remove water from "wet" organic liquids. The salts bond to water molecules to form hydrated salts that can easily be removed with a filter pipet (microscale) or by gravity filtration (miniscale).

A good drying agent should be fast acting. It should have a high capacity for reacting with water so that a small quantity of drying agent adsorbs a lot of water. Several common drying agents and their properties are detailed in Table 1I-2.

Because of its large capacity and ease of separation, sodium sulfate is the drying agent most frequently used in microscale experiments. Sodium sulfate and magnesium sulfate are commonly used for miniscale experiments.

How to Do Microscale Drying

Place the solution to be dried in a small Erlenmeyer flask or conical vial. Add a small amount of the drying agent (about a quarter of a tip of a spatula) to the solution and swirl. Observe carefully. If the drying agent clumps, add another small portion of the drying agent until the solution is clear and the additional drying agent stays free-flowing (the small particles stay suspended). The amount of drying agent required will depend upon the solvent. Diethyl ether dissolves more water than does an equal volume of methylene chloride or hexane. Let the solution stand for a few minutes (5–10 minutes if using sodium sulfate). Prepare a Pasteur filter pipet that has been fitted with a cotton plug. Squeeze the bulb to remove the air. Insert the pipet into the bottom of the conical vial or Erlenmeyer flask. Slowly release the bulb and carefully draw the liquid up into the pipet. Try to avoid drawing up the drying agent, if possible. However, any drying agent that is drawn up into the pipet will stick to the cotton plug. Drain the liquid into a clean vial or Erlenmeyer flask. Rinse the drying agent with additional small portions of solvent and combine the washings. Discard the drying agent according to the instructor's directions.

Table 1I-2   Properties of Common Drying Agents*

Drying Agent	Capacity	Speed	Comments
Calcium chloride (CaCl₂)	low	rapid	Cannot be used with compounds containing oxygen and nitrogen; used in drying tubes.
Magnesium sulfate (MgSO₄)	high	rapid	Suitable for all organic liquids; hydrated salt is fine powder so is sometimes difficult to separate from dried solvent.
Potassium carbonate (K₂CO₃)	moderate	moderate	Forms larger hydrated crystals, so is easily separated from the dried solvent; cannot be used with acidic compounds.
Sodium carbonate (Na₂CO₃)	moderate	moderate	Forms larger hydrated crystals, so is easily separated from the dried solvent; cannot be used for acidic compounds.
Sodium sulfate (Na₂SO₄)	high	relatively slow (5–10 minutes)	Easily filtered, used in both microscale and miniscale experiments; inexpensive.

Do Not Use Hydrated Salts for Drying.

Other drying agents used for drying tubes and solvents:

Drying Agent	Comments
Drierite (CaSO₄)	Frequently used in drying tubes to keep moisture from getting into a reaction; an indicator in the reagent changes color from blue (anhydrous form) to pink (hydrated form) when saturated with water.
Molecular sieves (Type 4A)	Composed of silicates that trap water molecules within the lattice; frequently used in bottles of solvents when anhydrous solvents are needed.

*All salts are anhydrous.

How to Do Miniscale Drying

Place the solution to be dried in an Erlenmeyer flask or beaker. Add a spatula-tip full of the drying agent to the solution. Swirl to suspend the particles. In the presence of water, the small particles of the drying agent clump together. Continue adding small portions of the drying agent until the solution is completely clear (no water droplets remain) or when additional drying agent is free flowing. Loosely stopper the flask and let the solution stand for 10–15 minutes. Meanwhile, prepare a gravity filtration apparatus. (See Technique F, Recrystallization, Filtration, and Sublimation). Pour the dried solution carefully through the filter paper. Rinse the flask and filter paper with additional portions of solvent and then combine the solvent washings.

Important Tips Concerning Drying Agents

1. A solvent that has been in contact with water is not considered to be dry unless it has been dried with a drying agent.
2. Exact amounts of drying agent are usually not specified in a procedure. The only way to know for sure how much drying agent to add is by careful addition and observation.

3. Do not add more drying agent than is necessary. The drying agent can adsorb the organic product as well as water.
4. Swirling the drying agent and the solution enhances the speed of the drying.
5. If a liquid dissolves the drying agent, that liquid is probably water. Check to see if the correct layer has been chosen following an extraction or steam distillation.
6. Be aware that different organic solvents absorb differing amounts of water, so they will require different amounts of drying agent. Diethyl ether partially dissolves some water and requires a lot of drying agent.

Microscale

Exercise I.1: Determining the Distribution Coefficient of Caffeine

Safety First!

Always wear eye protection in the laboratory.

Do not breathe methylene chloride vapors. Work in the hood.

Weigh out about 100 mg of caffeine; record the exact mass. Transfer the caffeine to a 5-mL conical vial. Using a calibrated pipet, add 1.0 mL of methylene chloride and 1.0 mL of water to the vial. Cap the vial and shake vigorously to mix the layers thoroughly and dissolve the caffeine. Cautiously unscrew the cap to vent and release the pressure. If all of the caffeine does not dissolve, add another 0.5 mL of both methylene chloride and water and shake again. Allow the layers to separate. Use a filter pipet (Technique F) to transfer the methylene chloride (lower layer) to a clean Erlenmeyer flask or vial. Be sure to transfer all of the methylene chloride, but no water. Add anhydrous sodium sulfate to the methylene chloride solution until no further clumping is observed. (This will take about the tip of a spatula full of sodium sulfate.) Let the solution stand for 5 minutes. With a clean, dry filter pipet, transfer the dried solution into a tared clean, dry 10-mL Erlenmeyer flask that contains a boiling chip. Rinse the drying agent remaining with a fresh portion of methylene chloride (about 0.5 mL); combine this rinse with the methylene chloride solution. Evaporate the solvent by placing the Erlenmeyer flask in a warm sand bath under the hood. Reweigh after cooling to room temperature.

Calculate the mass of caffeine extracted by methylene chloride. Calculate the mass of caffeine remaining in the water. (The mass of caffeine in the water will be the difference between the starting mass of caffeine and the mass in caffeine in methylene chloride.) Calculate the distribution coefficient of caffeine in the methylene chloride/water system.

Miniscale

Exercise I.2: Determining the Distribution Coefficient of Caffeine

Safety First!

Always wear eye protection in the laboratory.

Do not breathe methylene chloride vapors. Work in the hood.

Weigh out about 300 mg of caffeine; record the exact mass. Transfer the caffeine to a 25-mL Erlenmeyer flask. Using a calibrated pipet, add 10.0 mL of water to the flask. Swirl the flask to dissolve the caffeine. Pour the solution into a 50-mL or 125-mL separatory funnel that is supported in a ring stand. Make certain that the stopcock is closed before adding the solution. Now pipet 10.0 mL methylene chloride into the Erlenmeyer flask. Swirl the flask and pour the contents into the separatory funnel. Stopper the funnel. Partially invert the funnel and open the stopcock to release the pressure. Close the stopcock, shake or swirl the funnel gently several times, and vent again by inverting the funnel and opening the stopcock. Repeat this process several times. Replace the funnel in the ring and allow the layers to separate. Remove the stopper and open the stopcock to drain the lower methylene chloride layer into a clean, dry Erlenmeyer flask. Don't dispose of the aqueous layer until the experiment is finished. Use a spatula to add anhydrous sodium sulfate to the methylene chloride solution and swirl the flask. Continue adding small amounts of the drying agent until no further clumping is observed and some of the drying agent is free flowing. Stopper the flask with a cork and let it stand for 5 minutes. Gravity filter the dried solution into a tared clean, dry 25-mL Erlenmeyer flask that contains a boiling chip. Rinse the drying agent with a fresh portion of methylene chloride (about 1–2 mL) and add the rinse to the tared Erlenmeyer flask. Place the flask in a warm sand bath. Evaporate the solvent under the hood. Alternately, reduce the volume of the methylene chloride using a simple distillation apparatus. When the volume is reduced to 3–4 mL, transfer the solution to a tared Erlenmeyer flask that contains a boiling chip and evaporate the rest of the methylene chloride under the hood using a warm sand bath. Reweigh the flask.

Calculate the mass of caffeine extracted into methylene chloride. Calculate the mass of caffeine remaining in the water. (The mass of caffeine in the water will be the difference between the starting mass of caffeine and the mass of caffeine in methylene chloride.) Calculate the distribution coefficient of caffeine in the methylene chloride/water system.

Exercise I.3: Using Distribution Coefficients to Identify an Unknown Solid

Microscale

This exercise involves the extraction of an unknown solid in two different solvent systems: methylene chloride/water and ethyl acetate/water. The solid, which is either caffeine or resorcinol, will be identified by measuring the amount of the solid that dissolves in the organic solvent, calculating the amount of solid that remains in the aqueous (water) layer, calculating the distribution coefficient for each solvent system, and then comparing the calculated distribution coefficients with known values (shown in Table 1I-3). Caffeine is found in many soft drinks and beverages. Resorcinol is used in cosmetics and as a topical anesthetic.

Extraction Using Methylene Chloride/Water: Weigh out about 100 mg of the assigned solid; record the exact mass and record the unknown number. Transfer the solid to a 5-mL conical vial. Using a calibrated pipet, add 2.0 mL of methylene chloride and 2.0 mL of water to the vial. Cap the vial and shake gently to mix the layers. Cautiously unscrew the cap to vent and release the pressure. Tighten the cap and shake vigorously until all of the solid dissolves. Allow the layers to separate. Use a filter pipet (Technique F) to transfer the methylene chloride (lower layer) to a clean 25-mL Erlenmeyer flask. Be sure to transfer all of the methylene chloride, but no water. Add anhydrous sodium sulfate to the methylene chloride solution until no further clumping is observed. Let the solution stand for 5 minutes. With a clean, dry filter pipet, transfer the dried solution into a tared clean, dry 10-mL Erlenmeyer flask that contains a boiling chip. (If possible, dry this flask in the oven for 10 minutes; let cool to room temperature before weighing the flask.) Rinse the drying agent remaining with a fresh 1-mL portion of methylene chloride; combine this

Safety First!

Always wear eye protection in the laboratory.

Do not breathe methylene chloride vapors. Work in the hood.

Table 1I-3   Distribution Coefficient Values for Caffeine and Resorcinol in Two Different Solvent Systems.

Compound	K_D methylene chloride/water	K_D ethyl acetate/water
Caffeine	1.80	9.0
Resorcinol	0.07	6.6

rinse with the methylene chloride solution. Evaporate the solvent under the hood by placing the Erlenmeyer flask on a hot plate turned on low. Remove the flask from the hot plate and let cool to room temperature before weighing.

Extraction in Ethyl Acetate/Water: This extraction procedure varies slightly, because ethyl acetate is less dense than water. Weigh out about 100 mg of the assigned solid; record the exact mass and record the unknown number. Transfer the solid to a 5-mL conical vial. Using a calibrated pipet, add 2.0 mL of ethyl acetate and 2.0 mL of water to the vial. Cap the vial and shake it gently to mix the layers. Cautiously unscrew the cap to vent and release the pressure. Tighten the cap and shake vigorously until all of the solid dissolves. Allow the layers to separate. Ethyl acetate is less dense than water and will be the upper layer. However, in a microscale extraction, it is always the lower layer that is removed from the vial. Use a pipet (Technique F) to transfer the aqueous lower layer to a vial or flask. Then use a clean filter pipet to transfer the ethyl acetate to a clean 25-mL Erlenmeyer flask. Add anhydrous sodium sulfate to the ethyl acetate solution until no further clumping is observed. Let the solution stand for 5 minutes. With a clean, dry filter pipet, transfer the dried solution into a tared clean, dry 10-mL Erlenmeyer flask that contains a boiling chip. (If possible, dry this flask in the oven for 10 minutes; let cool to room temperature before weighing the flask.) Rinse the drying agent remaining with a fresh 1-mL portion of ethyl acetate; combine this rinse with the ethyl acetate solution. Evaporate the solvent under the hood by placing the Erlenmeyer flask on a hot plate turned on low. Remove the flask from the hot plate and let cool to room temperature before weighing.

Analysis: Determine the mass of the solid extracted into methylene chloride. Calculate the mass of solid remaining in the water. (The mass of solid in the water will be the difference between the starting mass of the solid and the mass in the solid in methylene chloride.) Calculate the distribution coefficient of the solid in the methylene chloride/water system. Repeat the analysis for the ethyl acetate system. Compare the calculated values with the actual values shown in Table 1I-3 and identify the unknown.

Note: Do not breathe ethyl acetate vapors. Work in the hood.

Questions

1. Approximately 1.0 g of caffeine will dissolve in 28 mL of methylene chloride and in 46 mL of water. Calculate the distribution coefficient of caffeine in this solvent system.

2. The K_D methylene chloride/water of an organic compound is 2.50. A solution is made by dissolving 48 mg of the compound in 10 mL of H_2O. How many milligrams of the compound will be extracted using:

    a. one portion of 10 mL of methylene chloride?

    b. two portions of 5 mL of methylene chloride?

3. What are four characteristics of a good extraction solvent?

4. *Library project*: Search for the method now commonly used to extract caffeine from coffee to manufacture decaffeinated coffee.

5. If too much drying agent is added to a solution, what can be done to correct the situation?

6. It has been suggested that drying agents can be collected after an experiment and the hydrated salt heated in an oven to drive off the water. The recycled drying agent can then be used again for another experiment. Is this a good idea? Give advantages and disadvantages of this proposal.

7. Cite advantages and disadvantages of using the following drying agents: sodium sulfate, magnesium sulfate, sodium carbonate, and potassium carbonate.

8. Drierite ($CaSO_4$) and calcium chloride are used in drying tubes to keep moisture out of reaction vessels. What properties are desirable for these agents?

9. The density of an aqueous solution increases as solutes such as salts are added. What bearing might this have on predicting whether the aqueous solution will be on the top or on the bottom for an extraction?

10. Look up the structures of resorcinol and caffeine. Which compound is expected to have the larger dipole? Explain.

11. Would it be possible to separate a mixture of caffeine and resorcinol using extraction? If so, suggest a method for doing so.

Technique J: Gas-Liquid Chromatography

Introduction

Chromatography is the separation of components of a mixture by differential adsorption between a stationary phase and a mobile phase. The word "chromatography," coined by Tswett around 1900, means to "write" in "color." Early chromatographic methods utilized paper as the stationary phase. The use of chromatography by analytical chemists began in the early 1950s and organic chemists followed soon afterward. Today, chromatography consists of a diverse collection of separation methods. All chromatographic techniques are based on a similar principle—components of a mixture can often be differentiated by exposure to two competing phases, a stationary phase and a mobile phase. Some components have little attraction for the stationary phase and are carried rapidly through the system with the mobile phase; other components adhere strongly to the stationary phase and have little attraction for the mobile phase.

The chromatographic methods used most frequently by organic chemists are gas-liquid chromatography, column chromatography, high-performance liquid chromatography, and thin-layer chromatography. Gas-liquid chromatography is used for separations of volatile or reasonably volatile organic liquids and solids. In gas-liquid chromatography, the components are partitioned between a liquid coating on the column (the stationary phase) and an inert gas (the mobile phase). In column and thin-layer chromatography, the components are partitioned between a solid stationary phase (like silica gel or alumina) and a liquid mobile phase (the solvent).

Gas-Liquid Chromatography Basics

Gas-liquid chromatography (GC) was invented in the early 1940s, but was not widely used until the late 1950s. It is now used universally in organic and analytical laboratories because most separations are rated at hundreds or thousands of theoretical plates–much superior to fractional distillation. In addition, the equipment is relatively inexpensive ($3,000 to $30,000), analysis times are short, and very small amounts of sample are required. GC can be used for both qualitative separations and quantitative analyses. These characteristics make GC an ideal tool for the microscale and miniscale organic laboratories. The stationary phase for GC is usually an organic polymer coated on the inside of a tube, such as a long capillary tube, and the mobile phase is an inert gas, such as helium.

A small volume (1–10 µL) of a mixture of volatile substances (usually dissolved in a solvent) is injected by syringe onto a heated column through which an inert carrier gas is flowing. The heat applied, as well as the gas flow, help the molecules from the sample travel through the column. Smaller, more volatile molecules generally emerge first from the opposite end of the column through an exit port and are detected. The detector is connected to a recording device, which shows a deflection when a sample passes the detector in proportion to the amount of sample detected. Compounds are eluted through an exit port either in an intact form or as combustion products, depending upon the type of detector used. A schematic diagram of a gas chromatograph is shown in Figure 1J-1.

Columns

Columns are of two main types: metal columns of $1/4$-inch, $1/8$-inch, or $1/16$-inch diameter that contain a polymer-coated, powdered solid support and glass columns that have very small diameters (capillary columns) that contain a fine polymer coating on the inside of the column. Column lengths range from 3 to 30 feet for metal columns and much longer (100 feet) for capillary columns.

The polymers used in GC columns are called stationary phase materials. The polymer coating aids in separating components by partially absorbing the compounds, which helps to selectively slow them down. The polymeric coatings may be polar, semipolar, or nonpolar. Examples are carbowax [$HO(CH_2-CH_2-O)_nH$], which is a polar stationary phase, and silicone polymers, such as SE 30 and Dow-Corning 200 (shown here), which are nonpolar stationary phases.

$$\left(\begin{array}{c} CH_3 \quad\quad CH_3 \\ | \quad\quad\quad | \\ -Si-O-Si-O- \\ | \quad\quad\quad | \\ CH_3 \quad\quad CH_3 \end{array}\right)_n$$

Detectors

As molecules emerge from the column, they are detected and recorded. A computer may be used to compile data furnished by the detector. Thermal conductivity detectors (TCD), flame ionization detectors (FID), and mass selective detectors (MSD) are common types of detectors.

The thermal conductivity detector, the most common type of detector, senses a difference in thermal conductivity of gases eluting from a GC column. Helium has a very high thermal conductivity and organic materials appearing in the effluent cause a decrease in the thermal conductivity. The lowered thermal conductivity slightly raises the temperature of the detector filament. This causes the electrical resistance of the filament to increase.

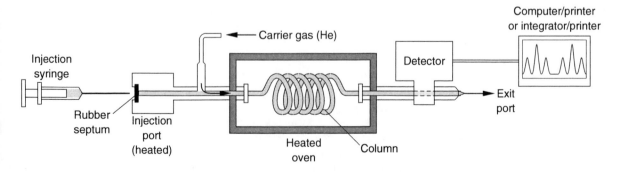

Figure 1J-1   Schematic drawing of a gas chromatograph

Technique J   *Gas-Liquid Chromatography*   **85**

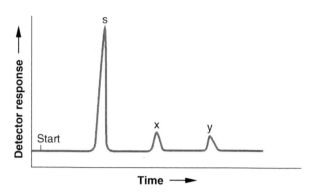

Figure 1J-2

Sample chromatogram

This change in electrical resistance is recorded as a peak on a chromatogram. The change in thermal conductivity is linear according to the number of molecules in the effluent.

Flame ionization detectors consist of a flame fueled by hydrogen gas. As organic molecules are eluted from the column, some are ionized by an ionization source. The intensity of ions is measured as current by an electrometer. The electrometer passes a signal to the recorder causing a peak in the chromaogram. FID detectors are very sensitive and can detect as little as 1 nanomol of an organic substance.

Mass selective detectors used in gas chromatography–mass spectrometry (GC/MS) are also extremely sensitive.

Chromatogram

A chromatogram is a plot of detector response versus time. A chromatogram for separation of two components, x and y, dissolved in solvent s, is shown in Figure 1J-2. The solvent is chosen so that it is usually eluted first. Common solvents are diethyl ether and acetone. Substance x is eluted before substance y.

Retention Time

The retention time (t_R) of a compound is the time elapsed from injection (t = 0) to the appearance of the peak. Retention times may be measured in seconds or minutes or cm, where the recorder chart speed is constant. Retention times are useful in identifying components of a mixture if samples of the pure compounds are available for comparison. The standards must be run under the same conditions as the mixture for direct comparison.

Retention times can be changed by switching columns, raising or lowering the column temperature, and increasing or decreasing the flow of carrier gas. It is common practice in the organic lab to note carefully all conditions used in operating the GC instrument.

Efficiency of Separation

Measuring the peak width (w) at the baseline of the peak allows evaluation of the efficiency of the process. The number of theoretical plates (N) and the height equivalent of a theoretical plate (HETP) may be calculated by measuring the height of the column (in cm) and using the equations given here. The smaller the value of y (narrow peak), the higher the efficiency. For high efficiency, N should be large and HETP should be small. Capillary columns are often rated at 1000 plates or more. Metal columns of small diameter (1/8 inch, 300 plates) are rated higher than those of larger diameter (1/4 inch, 100 plates).

$$N = 16 \, [t_R/w]^2$$

$$HETP = \text{length of column}/N$$

Calculation of the Number of Theoretical Plates

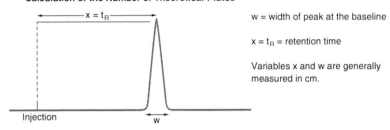

w = width of peak at the baseline

x = t_R = retention time

Variables x and w are generally measured in cm.

GC Separations

There are several factors that affect separation. These include carrier gas flow rate, column temperature, injector and exit port temperatures, detector temperature, amount of sample injected, length of column, diameter of column, and type of compound (polymer) used to coat the inside of the column. Of these factors, those associated with the column are critical.

The inner areas of all columns are coated with a polymeric stationary phase, which can be polar, semipolar, or nonpolar. A polar stationary phase has a high affinity for polar components and retains them on the column more than nonpolar components. Conversely, a nonpolar stationary phase retains nonpolar components more effectively than polar components. Changing the stationary phase will influence rates of elution of components of different polarities, resulting in differences in peak positions on chromatograms.

An example of an idealized separation of cyclohexane (bp 81°C) and ethanol (bp 78°C) illustrates the effect of the nature of the stationary phase. With a polar stationary phase, ethanol is retained and cyclohexane, which is not retained, is eluted first. A nonpolar stationary phase retains the cyclohexane so that ethanol is eluted first.

Longer columns, such as capillary columns, retain components longer and offer better separation. Slower flow rates of the carrier gas (the mobile phase) decrease elution rates of components, which can improve separations. Low temperatures also slow elution rates and can improve separation. Smaller amounts of sample give better separations, particularly if components have very similar retention times.

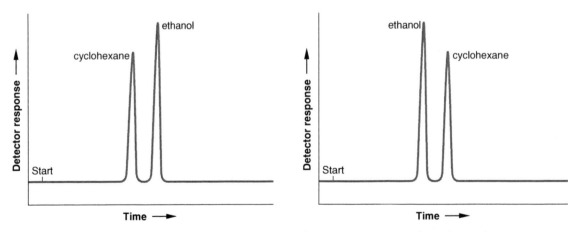

Separation using a polar stationary phase   Separation using a nonpolar stationary phase

When separating a mixture of two substances, it is desirable to achieve baseline separation. Baseline separation means having two totally separate peaks that show no overlap. Many times it is not possible to achieve baseline separation, as in the case of isomers or other compounds that have very similar boiling points. In such a case it is customary to express the degree of separation as resolution (R). Resolution can be calculated as shown, using the retention times of two components and the estimated peak widths at the baseline. It is desirable to have R values of 1.5 or greater for quantitative work. When R is less than 1, the calculated amounts of each component are approximate.

Calculation of Resolution, R

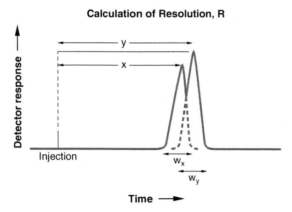

w = width of peak at the baseline

y = retention time of peak y

x = retention time of peak x

$\Delta t_R = y - x$

$R = 2\Delta t_R/(w_x + w_y)$

If R = 1, there is 98% separation.

Quantitative Analysis

The relative amount of each component may be calculated from areas using several different methods. Electronic integration is now common in most laboratories. With electronic integration, area percent values for each component of a mixture are output directly.

Mechanical methods can also be used. One of these methods is triangulation. The area of each peak is determined by measuring the peak height, and the peak width at half height, and then multiplying these two measurements to determine the area of each peak.

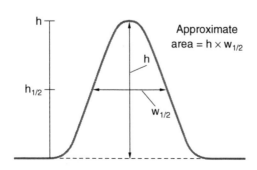

An earlier mechanical method was to employ a planimeter to trace each peak, noting the reading on the planimeter after measuring the perimeter of each peak. Still another method was to photocopy the chromatogram using high-quality paper. The peaks are each cut out and weighed. The area percent of each component can be found by dividing the weight of each component by the total of all weights and multiplying by 100.

Measurement of areas of overlapping peaks is best done by approximation. (If possible, it is best to avoid overlapping peaks by changing the temperature, the flow rate of carrier gas, or the column in order to increase resolution.) The example on page 87 shows how to use approximation. The inner line of the first peak is extended to the projection of the baseline and the same is done for the inner line of the second peak. Areas are then estimated using triangulation. Electronic integrators perform the approximation automatically.

Calculations Based on Weight Percent

Determining the areas beneath all of the peaks of a chromatogram enables the analyst to assign percentages to each of the components. This is called area normalization. The weight percent of component A is shown here.

$$\%A = \frac{\text{area of A}}{\text{total area}} \times 100$$

If a mixture of three components, A, B, and C, is analyzed, the weight percent of each component may be determined easily from the relative peak areas if the peaks are not overlapping and if the compounds have similar structures. Components that have different functionalities give different detector responses, making it necessary to apply correction factors prior to determining the weight percent of each component.

Relative detector response factors for different compounds can be determined by comparing peak areas of a mixture prepared by measuring out equal weights of each compound in the mixture. Dividing the area percent by the weight percent of each component gives a measure of relative sensitivity to the detector. A component giving a smaller response value means that the detector does not respond as much to it as a component with a higher value.

Sample Problem

A mixture containing acetone and pentane was analyzed by GC using an FID detector. The response factors for acetone and pentane, according to McNair and Bonelli (1960), are 0.49 and 1.04, respectively. The following data were obtained:

compound	area of peak
acetone	4.30 cm^2
pentane	2.20 cm^2

The equation used to solve for weight percent of each component in a mixture is given below:

$$\% \text{ component} = \frac{\text{corrected area of component}}{\sum \text{corrected areas of all components}} \times 100,$$

where the corrected areas are calculated by dividing the measured areas by the detector response

$$\text{corrected area of component} = \frac{\text{measured area of component}}{\text{detector response for that component}}$$

For the acetone-pentane mixture, the corrected area of acetone is 4.30 cm^2/ 0.49 = 8.8 cm^2 and the corrected area of pentane is 2.20 cm^2/1.04 = 2.1 cm^2. The sum of the corrected areas is 8.8 cm^2 + 2.1 cm^2 = 10.9 cm^2.

Therefore, the weight percent of acetone in the mixture is 8.8 cm^2/10.9 cm^2 × 100 = 80.7% and the weight percent of pentane is 19.3%. Without the correction factors the predicted weight percent values would be 66% acetone and 34% pentane, which is obviously very different from the values corrected for differential response of the detector. On the other hand, analysis of a mixture of heptane and pentane would give similar weight percent values with or without the detector response values factored in. Thermal conductivity detectors also have different responses for different substances.

How to Use the Gas Chromatograph

Column, carrier gas flow rate, column temperature, chart speed, and other parameters will usually be already chosen. Be sure to note these conditions. The detector and injection port temperatures are kept at a higher temperature than the column.

Liquids can be run neat or in a solution, while volatile solids are dissolved in a low-boiling solvent. Rinse the syringe several times with the sample or sample solution. Then fill the syringe. Make certain there are no air bubbles in the syringe. Then hold the syringe straight up and expel excess liquid, bringing the volume to the appropriate level (usually 1–5 µL). Insert the needle of the syringe into the center of the rubber septum by holding close to the end of the needle. Push the needle all the way into the septum until resistance is felt. Then gently but quickly depress the plunger of the syringe to inject the sample. (Be careful not to bend the needle since syringes are expensive. The instructor will demonstrate this technique.) Start the chart paper as soon as the sample is injected. Remove the syringe by pulling straight out. Rinse the syringe several times with acetone and let dry. When the components have eluted from the column, stop the chart recorder.

If the peaks are too small or too large, adjust the attenuation or change the amount of sample injected. An integrator attached to a recorder will furnish percentages of components for each analysis. If no integrator is available, individual peaks may be cut out from the chart pages and weighed. Alternatively, peak width at half height times the height may be calculated for each peak and relative percentage of each component determined (p. 87). Percentages for closely overlapping peaks are difficult to determine by these methods.

To identify components of a mixture, standards should be injected under the same set of conditions. Alternately, it is possible to "spike" a mixture by adding some of the pure component to the mixture and rerunning the chromatogram. The peak that grows in size relative to the others corresponds to the standard injected.

Exercise J.1: Determining Relative Detector Response Factors in GC

Safety First!

Always wear eye protection in the laboratory.

Obtain a sample of a mixture containing equal masses of 1-butanol (bp 117°C), 2-butanone (bp 82°C), and methyl acetate (bp 58°C). These compounds were chosen because they have different functional groups, but similar molecular weights. Carefully inject 1–2 µL of the mixture and record the chromatogram. Note and record the column temperature, flow rate of the carrier gas, column polarity, and other column properties. If necessary, adjust the attenuation so that all three peaks fit on the paper. Measure the area of each peak. In order to identify the compound corresponding to each peak, inject 1–2 µL aliquots of pure 1-butanol, 2-butanone, and methyl acetate and compare retention times. Determine the relative mass percent of each component. Determine the relative detector response factor of each compound by dividing the experimental mass percent (from normalized peak areas) by the actual mass percent of each component in the mixture (33.3%).

Exercise J.2: Determining Mass Percent of a Mixture Using GC

Obtain a sample of a mixture containing 1-butanol (bp 117°C), 2-butanone (bp 82°C), and methyl acetate (58°C). Record the unknown number of the sample. Carefully inject 1–2 μL of the mixture and record the chromatogram. If necessary, adjust the attenuation so that all three peaks fit on the paper. Record the column temperature, flow rate of the carrier gas, column polarity, and other conditions as noted by the instructor. Measure the area of each peak. If necessary, inject 1–2 μL aliquots of the pure compounds in order to identify the peak associated with each compound. Using the detector response factors for each component determined in Exercise J.1, calculate the corrected area for each component by dividing the measured area of the component by the detector response factor for that component. (If Exercise J.1 was not done, the instructor will provide the detector response factors.) Determine the mass percent of the mixture by dividing the corrected area for each component by the sum of the corrected areas for all components. If more than one GC instrument is available for use, repeat the analysis of the mixture using (1) a higher column temperature; (2) a faster flow rate for the carrier gas; or (3) a different column.

Exercise J.3: Determining Mass Percent of a Mixture of Alcohols

Safety First!

Always wear eye protection in the laboratory.

Obtain a mixture of three alcohols: 2-propanol (bp 82°C), 1-propanol (bp 97°C), and 1-butanol (bp 117°C). Carefully inject 1–2 μL of the mixture and record the chromatogram. If necessary, adjust the attenuation so that all three peaks fit on the paper. Record the column temperature, flow rate of the carrier gas, column polarity, and other conditions as noted by the instructor. Measure the area of each peak. In order to identify the alcohol corresponding to each peak, inject 1–2 μL aliquots of the pure alcohols and compare retention times. Calculate the mass percent of each component in the mixture of alcohols. (Assume the detector response is equal for all of the components.) Explain the trend in order of elution for the column used.

If more than one GC instrument is available for use, repeat the analysis of the mixture using (1) a higher column temperature; (2) a faster flow rate for the carrier gas; or (3) a different column.

Questions

1. Explain the principle of operation of a thermal conductivity detector (TCD).

2. Explain the relationship between HETP and column length.

3. When analyzing the chromatogram obtained from a binary (two-component) mixture, it is necessary to know which peak corresponds to component A and which to component B. Explain how this can be done using the GC instrument.

4. What type of detector should be used if components are to be collected while they are being analyzed by GC? Explain.

5. What is the mobile phase used in gas chromatography? What is the stationary phase? Give an example of a stationary phase.

6. How is resolution affected by lowering the column temperature? By lengthening the column?

7. Explain how the amount of sample injected onto a column affects the separation of a two-component mixture.

8. Calculate resolution (R) and the relative amounts of each component for the chromatogram shown below.

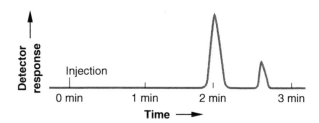

9. A chromatogram of a mixture of components A, B, and C is given below. Suggest methods for improving resolution.

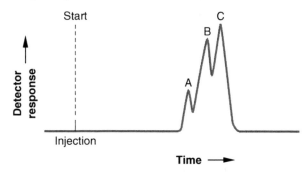

10. For each of the pairs of compounds below, indicate whether the relative detector response factors would be expected to be similar or different. Explain your reasoning.

    a. decane (MW 142) and 1-nonanol (MW 144)

    b. 2-propanol (bp 82°C) and 1-butanol (bp 117°C)

    c. 1-butanol (MW 74, bp 117°C) and diethyl ether (MW 74, bp 35°C)

11. What effect would each of the following have on the retention times?

    a. increase the column temperature

    b. increase the flow rate of the carrier gas

    c. use a more polar column

12. Explain why the alcohols in Exercise J3 are assumed to have equivalent response to the detector.

Reference

McNair, H. M., and Bonelli, E. J. *Basic Gas Chromatography. 5th ed.* Walnut Creek, CA: Varian Aerograph, 1960.

Technique K: Thin-Layer, Column, and High-Performance Liquid Chromatography

Introduction

Chromatographic techniques are used extensively in the organic laboratory for both qualitative separations and quantitative analysis. A thorough understanding of the various types of chromatography is essential. Thin-layer chromatography (TLC) is used to determine the purity of a compound, to evaluate how far a reaction has proceeded, and to analyze the composition of a mixture, while column chromatography is used to physically separate components of a mixture. High-pressure liquid chromatography (HPLC) can be used for both qualitative and quantitative analysis.

All chromatographic techniques are based on a similar principle: components of a mixture can often be differentiated by exposure to two competing phases. In TLC, the stationary phase is a polar adsorbent, such as silica gel or alumina, which has been coated onto a glass or plastic plate. The mobile phase is an organic solvent or mixture of solvents. The liquid moves up the plate by capillary action. Column chromatography is similar to TLC, with a stationary phase of silica gel or alumina and a mobile liquid phase, but differs in that the liquid travels down the column. A polymer-coated adsorbent is the stationary phase in HPLC. The mobile liquid phase in HPLC is forced through a small diameter column by a pump at high pressure.

Introduction to Thin-Layer Chromatography (TLC)

TLC is the separation of moderately volatile or nonvolatile substances based upon differential adsorption on an inert solid (the stationary phase) immersed in an organic solvent or solvent mixture (the mobile phase). The components are distributed between the stationary phase (usually silica gel or alumina) and the solvent depending upon the polarities of the compound and solvent. The compounds are carried up the plate (ascending chromatography) at a rate dependent upon the nature of the compounds and the solvent.

Compounds are separated by adsorption chromatography based upon differential attachment of molecules to the adsorbent and the polarity of the solvent used for the separation as shown in Figure 1K-1. Polar compounds are strongly attracted to and held by a polar adsorbent. Nonpolar compounds are held weakly. When a nonpolar solvent is passed

Figure 1K-1

Adsorption equilibrium for molecules between adsorbent and solvent

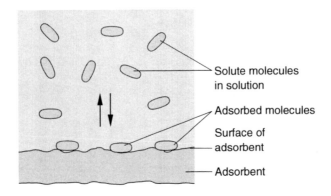

Solute molecules in solution

Adsorbed molecules

Surface of adsorbent

Adsorbent

through the adsorbent, nonpolar compounds are released easily, but polar compounds are retained. When a moderately polar solvent is passed through the adsorbent, both nonpolar and polar compounds are released, but the nonpolar compounds move faster because there is still an attraction between the polar compounds and the polar adsorbent. In general, nonpolar compounds move faster than polar compounds for TLC on silica gel or alumina.

Polarity of Solvents Used for Adsorption Chromatography

Solvents are rated according to their polarities. Common solvents are listed below from most polar to least polar.

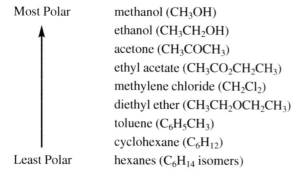

Most Polar	methanol (CH_3OH)
	ethanol (CH_3CH_2OH)
	acetone (CH_3COCH_3)
	ethyl acetate ($CH_3CO_2CH_2CH_3$)
	methylene chloride (CH_2Cl_2)
	diethyl ether ($CH_3CH_2OCH_2CH_3$)
	toluene ($C_6H_5CH_3$)
	cyclohexane (C_6H_{12})
Least Polar	hexanes (C_6H_{14} isomers)

If a polar compound moves too slowly in a nonpolar solvent, switching to a more polar solvent will cause the compound to move faster. If a nonpolar compound moves too fast on TLC, switching to a less polar solvent will cause the compound to move slower. The polarity of the solvent system can also be varied by mixing miscible solvents to give the desired separation.

Calculating R_f Values

The distance traveled by each component is expressed as a rate or retardation factor (R_f). R_f values are calculated by dividing the distance traveled by a component by the distance between the origin and the solvent front (distance traveled by the solvent). Hence all R_f values will fall between 0 and 1. R_f values are measured from the origin where the initial spot was applied to the center of the spot.

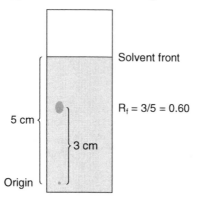

In general, R_f values on silica gel or alumina are decreased by decreasing the polarity of the solvent and increased by increasing the solvent polarity. The main objective in TLC analysis is to obtain separation of components of a mixture. A solvent is selected to give a range of R_f values. If a single solvent fails to give adequate separation, a solvent mixture should be used. Examples of TLC that show the effect of solvent polarity are given below:

Example 1 The compounds 9-fluorenone, *m*-dinitrobenzene, and azobenzene are moderately polar. The structures are shown below:

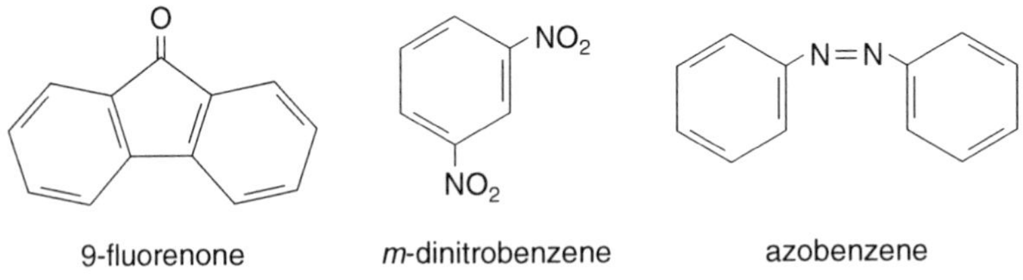

9-fluorenone   *m*-dinitrobenzene   azobenzene

In order to separate a mixture of these compounds effectively, toluene, which is a relatively nonpolar solvent, was chosen. Solutions of each of the three pure compounds were spotted on the silica gel plate as well as a solution containing a mixture of the three compounds.

Successful separation was achieved using toluene. The separation obtained is very satisfactory since all R_f values are considerably different from one another, as shown in Table 1K-1. The silica gel TLC of 9-fluorenone, *m*-dinitrobenzene, azobenzene, and a mixture of the three components eluted with toluene is shown here.

Example 2 For the TLC separation of benzaldoxime (B) and *p*-tolualdoxime (T), hexane failed to move the compounds significantly, but ethyl acetate moved both compounds too fast, giving little separation. In this case, a mixed solvent system containing both hexane and ethyl acetate gave better results, moving both compounds about midway up the plate, while also achieving different R_f values for B and T. The exact per-

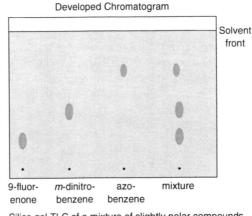

Silica gel TLC of a mixture of slightly polar compounds
and each of the pure components using toluene as solvent

Table 1K-1 R_f Values for Example 1

Compound	TLC in toluene	
	Distance from origin (cm)	**R_f value**
9-fluorenone	1.6	0.25
m-dinitrobenzene	2.9	0.47
azobenzene	4.3	0.70
solvent front	6.2	1.00

centages of a mixed solvent system are best determined by trial and error. In this case, the optimal mixture was 70% hexane/30% ethyl acetate.

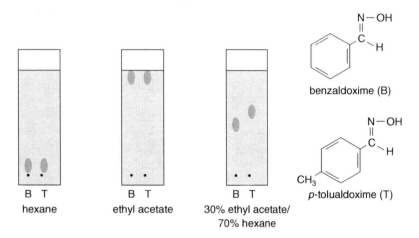

benzaldoxime (B)

p-tolualdoxime (T)

Resolution

In TLC, it is highly desirable to avoid overlapping of spots in the developed chromatogram, just as it was desirable to avoid overlapping peaks in GC. In GC, resolution can be improved by lowering the column temperature, decreasing the carrier gas flow rate, and using a different column or longer column. In TLC, resolution can be increased by varying the nature of the eluting solvent or by changing the adsorbent.

Resolution can be determined from the developed chromatogram by measuring the distance from the origin to the center of each spot (t_R) and measuring the height of each spot (h):

$$\text{Resolution (R)} = 2\left[\frac{\Delta t_R}{h_A + h_B}\right]$$

This is illustrated for the two-component mixture shown below.

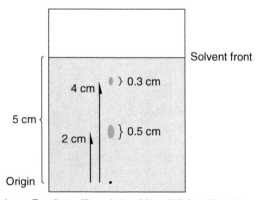

Resolution = R = 2 Δt_R/(h$_A$ + h$_B$) = 2(4 − 2)/(.3 + .5) = 4/.8 = 5

Good separation of components by TLC can be determined by looking at the spots on the developed plate. Calculation of R is not necessary unless results of several different eluting solvents are being compared. The best solvents have the highest R values.

Materials and Methods in TLC

Adsorbent

The most frequently used adsorbents are silica gel (SiO_2) and alumina (Al_2O_3), which are coated onto a plastic or glass support. TLC plates may be purchased from commercial vendors or they may be homemade. Commercial plates have adsorbents bound to a plastic, glass, or aluminum sheet as a backbone. The binder is calcium sulfate. The adsorbent is very uniform, about 0.1–0.2 mm thick. Homemade plates are usually made by dipping glass microscope slides into mixtures of adsorbent and binder in aqueous solution. Homemade plates are not usually as uniform in thickness as commercial plates. However, since TLC is generally used qualitatively rather than quantitatively, it is not so critical that the thickness of the layer be that uniform. Coated microscope slides are wiped clean on one side and the coated side is left to dry. These plates may be used directly for TLC. Commercial plates may be sized appropriately using scissors or a glass cutter.

Sample Application

Dots (in pencil) are marked uniformly along one of the narrow edges of the plate near the bottom at intervals of about 1–2 cm. Solutions of samples are spotted individually at each of the marks and the solvent is allowed to dry. The diameter of the residue from a spotted solution should be kept as small as possible to minimize diffusion effects. Capillary tubes or Pasteur pipets that have been drawn out in a flame are used as applicators. The very small openings in these drawn-out tubes permit application of very small amounts of solution.

Development

The development chamber can be a beaker covered by a watch glass or a jar with a screw-top cap. The chamber should be equilibrated before use by placing the developing solvent and a piece of filter paper in the chamber and capping the chamber. The chamber should stand undisturbed for 5–10 minutes to saturate the chamber with solvent vapors. The plate is put into the developing chamber after making certain that the level of the solvent is below that of the applied compounds on the plate. As the chromatogram is developed, the solvent advances up the plate through capillary action. Unless colored compounds are being separated (such as dyes in inks), the components cannot be visualized. The plate is left in the developing chamber until the level of the solvent is about 2 cm from the top of the plate. Then the plate is removed from the chamber, the solvent line is marked immediately with pencil, and the plate is allowed to dry.

Don't move the solvent chamber during chromatography.

Visualization

Because most organic compounds are not colored, the spots must be visualized using a UV light, an iodine chamber, or an indicator spray. Certain substances, such as aromatic compounds, absorb ultraviolet light and appear as purple spots. Commercial plates often contain a fluorescent dye that gives a light green background when exposed to UV radiation. Compounds that do not absorb UV light must be viewed in another way, such as placing the plate in an enclosed chamber containing solid iodine crystals. Most organic substances form colored complexes with iodine. After a few minutes, organic compounds on the developed plate begin to appear as brown spots. The effect is reversible over time after removal from the iodine chamber, so spots should be circled. Another option for visualizing spots is to spray the plate with a reagent that will cause development of a color. A commonly used spray is anisaldehyde-H_2SO_4, which gives colored spots for alcohols and certain other compounds.

The overall TLC procedure is summarized in Figure 1K-2. (a) A solution is spotted at the origin on a TLC plate, using a drawn capillary tube. (b) The plate is placed in a development chamber containing solvent. The level of the solvent is below the origin. (c) The solvent front is marked immediately upon removing the developed TLC plate from the development chamber. The dried TLC plate is visualized and spots are circled.

Introduction to Column Chromatography

Column chromatography using silica gel or alumina works like TLC except that solvents are passed down through the adsorbent holding the mixture to be separated (descending chromatography). Column chromatography may be thought of as a preparative version of TLC that permits separation and isolation of products by collection of eluted fractions. One major difference is that the sample is loaded at the top of an adsorbent, such as silica gel, and solvent is drained through a "column" of adsorbent, with components of the sample mixture being eluted from the bottom of the column. The relative speeds that components travel are similar to the relative R_f values in TLC. Thus, nonpolar components travel faster down the column than do polar components and are eluted first. There are several different types of column chromatography.

Gravity Column Chromatography

Gravity column chromatography is frequently used in the organic lab. A sample is applied to the top of a column filled with an adsorbent such as silica gel or alumina. Solvent is added to the top of the column. Components of the sample travel down the column at different rates, depending upon the polarity of the compounds, the polarity of the solvent and the nature of the adsorbent. Fractions are collected as the solvent continues to be added at the top and eluted at the bottom. After the first component is completely eluted, the solvent polarity can be increased so that a second component may be eluted faster.

Dry-Column Chromatography

Another type of column chromatography is dry-column chromatography. In dry-column chromatography, a solvent is chosen so as to spread out the components in a series of

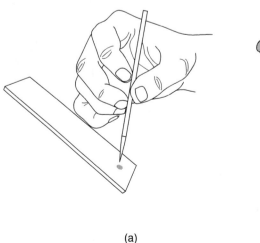

(a)

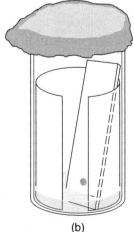

(b)

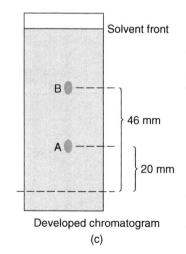

Solvent front

B

46 mm

A

20 mm

Developed chromatogram

(c)

Figure 1K-2   Procedure for TLC

bands. The column is packed and the sample is added to the top of the column. The chosen solvent is added only until the first drops of solvent reach the bottom of the column. No more solvent is then added. The column is then slit from stem to stern. A disposable plastic or nylon column works best here. Nylon is nice because it doesn't absorb UV light. The individual regions of adsorbent that absorb UV light are collected and the components are eluted with an appropriate solvent and filtered. The solvent is evaporated and the individual components are then isolated and purified.

Other Types of Column Chromatography

Ion exchange chromatography and size-exclusion gel permeation chromatography are commonly used in analytical and biochemistry laboratories. They are less frequently used in organic laboratories.

How to Do a Miniscale Gravity Column Chromatography

Preparing the Column

The chromatography column is usually a long glass tube, with a stopcock at the bottom that can be opened or closed.

Make sure that the column is clean and dry. Place a wad of cotton or glass wool in the bottom of the column, then add a layer of sand. The cotton plug and sand prevent loss of adsorbent through the stopcock and also keep the stopcock clear of particles. Next measure out the adsorbent into a beaker. The amount of adsorbent you need depends upon the difficulty of separation. In general, you will need about 10 g of adsorbent per 100 mg of sample to be separated. However, if the separation is an easy one (one polar component mixed with one nonpolar component), you will need less adsorbent. Pour the adsorbent into the column through a funnel. This should be done in the hood to avoid breathing in the fine particles of adsorbent. Tamp the side of the column gently to produce even packing of the adsorbent in the column. Now carefully pour the solvent into the column. Silica gel and alumina swell and give off heat as they take up the solvent. To eliminate any air pockets that may form as the solvent travels through the column, gently tamp on the column. Drain the solvent until the level of the solvent is to the top of the adsorbent. An example of a column prepared in this way is shown in Figure 1K-3.

Miniscale

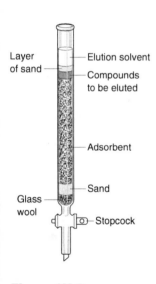

Layer of sand — Elution solvent

— Compounds to be eluted

— Adsorbent

— Sand

Glass wool

— Stopcock

Figure 1K-3

Chromatography column

Applying the Sample to the Column

If the sample is a liquid, add it directly to the top of the adsorbent. If the sample is a solid, dissolve it in a minimum amount of the eluting solvent and apply it carefully and evenly to the adsorbent using a pipet and bulb. Add a second layer of sand to prevent the adsorbent and sample from being disturbed.

Elution of the Sample

Choose an eluting solvent that is relatively nonpolar, but polar enough to move the least polar component of a mixture. Carefully add a pool of solvent and open the stopcock. Drain the solvent into collecting flasks or vials, called fractions. The number of fractions required will vary depending upon the separation. Add fresh solvent as necessary so that the level of solvent is always above the level of the sand. After the first component has been eluted, increase the polarity of the solvent to elute subsequent components.

If the components are colored, you can follow the progress of the separation visually. With colorless compounds, you must use TLC to determine which fractions contain the desired components. Pool the appropriate fractions and then remove the solvent by evaporation or distillation, leaving the component behind as a residue. The process of elution and collection is illustrated in Figure 1K-4.

How to Do Microscale Column Chromatography

Microscale

The procedure for microscale column chromatography is similar to that of miniscale. The procedure utilizes a Pasteur pipet, although a straw or plastic tube may be substituted.

Place a small wad of cotton or glass wool inside the tube and push it near the bottom of the tube, using a copper wire. Add a small layer of sand, followed by a layer of the adsorbent. The adsorbent should weigh about 100 times the sample weight (1 g adsorbent per 10 mg of sample). Add solvent until drops come out the bottom and the solvent level is flush with the level of the silica gel.

Immediately apply the sample to the top of the adsorbent. If the sample is a liquid, add it directly to the top of the column. If the sample is a solid or a thick oil, dissolve it in a minimum amount of solvent and add it to the adsorbent, using a pipet.

Add solvent to the top of the tube. The solvent should be polar enough to cause one of the components of the sample mixture to move. Collect fractions in flasks or test tubes. After the first component has eluted, increase solvent polarity to elute each subsequent component. Pool the appropriate fractions and then remove the solvent by evaporation under a hood. A microscale gravity column is illustrated in Figure 1K-5.

Introduction to High-Performance Liquid Chromatography

High-performance liquid chromatography (HPLC) can also be used to separate mixtures. HPLC is most useful as a quantitative analytical method, much the same as GC. The method resembles GC, but instead of a carrier gas, a solvent is used as the mobile phase. The most common detector uses UV detection.

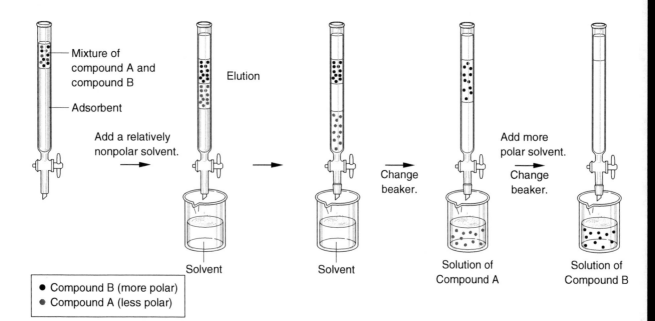

Figure 1K-4   Procedure for chromatographic separation of a two-component mixture

Organic Chemistry Laboratory CHM 375 & CHM 376

Figure 1K-5

Microscale gravity
column

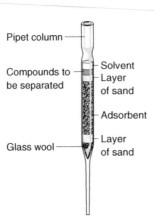

In HPLC, a small volume (1–2 mL) of a sample solution is injected by syringe onto the column, while a solvent mixture (mobile phase) passes through the column that contains a finely divided packing material. Solvent is forced through the column using a high-pressure pumping system. Elution may be accomplished using a simple solvent or solvent mixture (isocratic separation) or by gradually changing the solvent composition (gradient elution). Solvents used for HPLC must be ultra-pure HPLC-grade solvents. Water should be doubly deionized.

A major difference between HPLC separations and adsorption chromatographic separations is that most HPLC separations are accomplished using a reversed-phase stationary phase. (Reversed-phase TLC plates are also commercially available.) This means that polar components are eluted first and nonpolar components last. Reversed-phase columns contain finely divided silica gel particles chemically bonded to C-18 (or C-8) molecules. Nonpolar components dissolve well in the nonpolar C-18 coating. Starting with a very polar solvent such as water encourages elution of polar compounds. Gradually an organic solvent is mixed in, which eventually draws off the less-polar components. Analysis of components of chromatograms is done the same as in GC. A schematic of an HPLC system is shown in Figure 1K-6.

Figure 1K-6

Schematic of HPLC
instrument

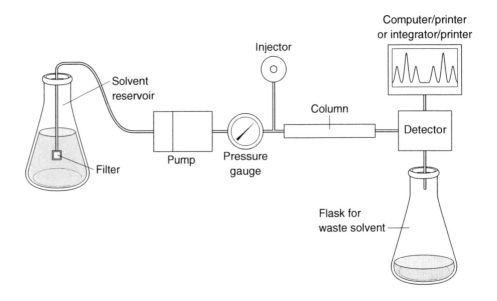

Exercise K.1: Analysis of Analgesic Tablets by TLC

Over-the-counter pain medications, such as Excedrin, Tylenol, or Advil, commonly contain aspirin, ibuprofen, acetaminophen, and/or caffeine (in addition to inert materials). TLC can be used to determine whether an analgesic tablet contains one or more of these active ingredients.

Obtain an analgesic tablet from the instructor. With a mortar and pestle, pulverize the tablet. Dissolve 1–2 mg of the powder in 0.5 mL methylene chloride. If the solid does not dissolve, add ethanol dropwise. Similarly prepare solutions of aspirin, ibuprofen, acetominophen, and caffeine. Obtain a silica gel TLC plate (5–10 cm or similar), development chamber (400-mL beaker, filter paper, and watch glass), and a ruler. Pour 8–10 mL of ethyl acetate into the development chamber and place the watch glass on top.

With a pencil, draw a faint line 1 cm from the bottom of the TLC plate, being careful not to break the silica gel. Make five dots on this line (called the "origin") to indicate where the mixture and standards will be applied. With a capillary tube, apply a tiny drop of each solution at the origin and air dry. Place the TLC plate in the developing chamber, making certain that the level of the solvent is below the origin. Replace the watchglass. When the level of the solvent is near the top of the plate, remove the plate, rapidly mark the solvent front and let the plate air dry. Visualize under UV light or in an iodine chamber and circle each spot. Calculate R_f values of the analgesic and of caffeine, ibuprofen, aspirin, and acetaminophen. List the active ingredient(s) found in the signed analgesic tablet.

Safety First!

Always wear eye protection in the laboratory.

Caution: Do not look at the UV light.

Exercise K.2: Separating Ferrocene and Acetylferrocene Using Column Chromatography

Microscale

Obtain a solid mixture of ferrocene and acetylferrocene from the instructor. Weigh out 30–40 mg of the mixture into a tared vial and record the exact mass. Dissolve the mixture in 4–5 drops of methylene chloride. Cap the vial until ready to use.

To prepare the column, obtain a Pasteur pipet, a small piece of glass wool, sand, and silica gel. Place a glass-wool plug in the bottom of the pipet. Pour in a small layer of sand. Fill the pipet about two-thirds full with silica gel. With a clean pipet, apply the solution of unknown evenly to the top of the silica gel. Rinse the vial with 1–2 drops of methylene chloride and add to the column. (Alternatively, add the solid sample directly to the top of the silica gel.) Pour a small layer of sand on top of the sample. This will keep the sample from being disturbed as solvent is added to the column.

Carefully add hexane to the top of the column. The hexane will drain through the column and should be collected in small vials or test tubes. Continue to add solvent so that the column never dries out. As the hexane moves down the column, the sample will begin to separate and will appear as separate bands in the silica gel. When one of the colored bands is at the bottom of the column, change collection vials and collect the colored effluent in a tared vial. When this component has been eluted from the column, the polarity of the solvent should be increased in order to hasten the elution of any other component. Pour a mixture of 1:1 hexane/ethyl acetate in the column and watch the rate at which the band moves through the column. Less time is needed if the solvent is changed to pure ethyl acetate. Collect the effluent in a different vial. Assess the results of the chromatographic separation by running two TLC plates using 10% ethyl

Safety First!

Always wear eye protection in the laboratory.

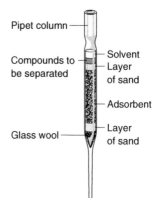

Pipet column —

Compounds to be separated

— Solvent

— Layer of sand

— Adsorbent

Glass wool —

— Layer of sand

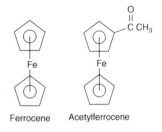

Ferrocene   Acetylferrocene

acetate/hexanes and 50% ethyl acetate/hexanes as eluents. Spot each product fraction and determine the effectiveness of the separation process.

Put the tared vials in a small beaker and set them under the hood while the solvent evaporates. Alternately, the vials may be heated on a sand bath or heat block under the hood. Using a stream of dry air or nitrogen will hasten the evaporation. Reweigh the vials and calculate the mass of each component eluted from the column. Return any unused solid to the instructor. Place solvents in the appropriately labeled bottle for recycling.

Miniscale

Exercise K.3: Separating Ferrocene and Acetylferrocene Using Column Chromatography

Safety First!

Always wear eye protection in the laboratory.

Obtain a solid mixture of ferrocene and acetylferrocene from the instructor. Weigh out 300 mg of the mixture into a small vial and record the exact mass. Dissolve the solid in 0.5 mL of methylene chloride. Cap the vial until ready to use.

To prepare the column, obtain a column or buret, a small piece of glass wool, sand, and silica gel. Make a glass-wool plug in the bottom of the column. Pour in a small layer of sand. Fill the column about two-thirds full with silica gel. Pour hexane into the top of the column, being careful not to disturb the layer of silica gel. Drain the hexane until the eluent level is at the top of the silica gel. With a clean pipet, apply the solution of ferrocene and acetylferrocene evenly to the top of the silica gel. Rinse the vial with 1–2 drops of methylene chloride and add it to the column. Pour a small layer of sand on top of the sample. The sand will keep the sample from being disturbed as solvent is added to the column.

Carefully add hexane to the top of the column. The hexane will drain through the column and should be collected in a flask or beaker. Continue to add solvent so that the column never dries out. As the hexane moves down the column, the sample will begin to separate and will appear as separate bands in the silica gel. When one of the colored bands is at the bottom of the column, change collection flasks and collect the colored effluent in a tared flask. When this component has eluted from the column, the polarity of the solvent should be increased in order to hasten the elution of any other component. Pour a mixture of 1:1 hexane/ethyl acetate into the column and watch the rate at which the band moves through the column. Less time is needed if the solvent is changed to pure ethyl acetate. Collect the effluent in a different flask. Evaporate the solvent under the hood using a warm sand bath. Reweigh the flasks and calculate the mass of each component. Return any unused solid to the instructor. Place solvents in the appropriately labeled bottle for recycling.

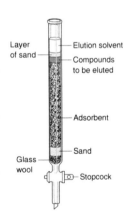

Layer of sand — Elution solvent
— Compounds to be eluted
— Adsorbent
— Sand
Glass wool — Stopcock

Exercise K.4: HPLC Analysis of Benzaldehyde and Benzyl Alcohol

Safety First!

Always wear eye protection in the laboratory.

Dissolve 2 μL of a 1:1 mixture of benzaldehyde and benzyl alcohol in 2 mL of acetonitrile. Similarly prepare a standard solution of benzyl alcohol or benzaldehyde. The instructor will demonstrate the use of the HPLC. Pump the solvent system (acetonitrile/water) through a C-18 reversed-phase HPLC column for 5 minutes at a flow rate of 1 mL/minute. Use a syringe to draw up 1–2 μL of the sample solution according to directions of the instructor and inject it onto the column. Record the chromatogram until both components have eluted from the column. The chromatogram is monitored by UV detection at 254 nm. When the sample has eluted from the HPLC, inject 1–2 μL of the standard solution and record the chromatogram. Based on the retention times of the components of the mixture and the retention times of the standard, identify each component of the mixture. Measure the areas of each peak and determine the relative mass percent of each component. (Molar absorptivities of the two components are about the same at 254 nm.)

Benzaldehyde

Benzyl alcohol

Questions

1. List three factors that affect R_f values in adsorption TLC. Explain.

2. Explain how to prepare sample solutions and capillary applicators.

3. Describe the basic principle underlying all chromatographic processes.

4. Predict the order of elution for the silica gel adsorption TLC separation of the mixture containing benzyl alcohol, benzaldehyde, and benzoic acid using methylene chloride solvent. Explain.

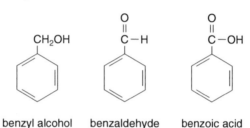

benzyl alcohol   benzaldehyde   benzoic acid

5. The resolution calculated for the TLC separation of a two-component mixture is determined to be equal to 2.0. Does this represent good separation or not? Explain.

6. When should a mixed-solvent system be used for TLC? Explain.

7. Is the order of elution of the components the same for TLC as for column chromatography?

8. Explain how the various fractions can be analyzed from a gravity column.

9. What chromatographic technique would be useful:

   a. to determine whether a nonvolatile compound is pure?

   b. to separate a mixture of two nonvolatile solids?

   c. to determine whether a reaction is complete?

10. Caffeine absorbs UV light. Describe how to determine if a cup of coffee is caffeinated or decaffeinated using HPLC.

Technique L: Polarimetry

Optical activity is a physical property of chiral molecules. Chiral molecules lack planes of symmetry and may exist as two or more stereoisomers. Stereoisomers that rotate the plane of plane-polarized light in equal but opposite directions are called enantiomers. Enantiomers have nonsuperimposable mirror-image structures. Enantiomers have identical physical properties, including the same boiling and melting points, except for rotation of the plane of plane-polarized light. Specific rotations [α] of enantiomers are equal, but opposite. One enantiomer has a positive rotation, indicating rotation of plane-polarized light to the right. The other enantiomer has a negative rotation, indicating rotation of the plane of plane-polarized light to the left.

The technique known as polarimetry is used to measure the optical rotation of liquids and solutions. Only optically active solutions can give readings of optical rotation other than 0°. Common solvents, such as water, methanol, ethanol, and ethyl acetate are not chiral and are not optically active. They may be used to prepare solutions of optically active substances for measurement of optical rotation using a polarimeter. The yellow light of a sodium lamp (sodium D line) is the accepted type of light to measure optical rotations.

The optical rotation of a chiral liquid or of a chiral substance in solution is called the observed rotation α. The observed rotation is read directly from a polarimeter and is related to the specific rotation $[\alpha]_D$ (a physical constant for the substance) according to Equation (1.7):

(1.7)
$$[\alpha]_D = \frac{\alpha}{c \times l}$$

where c is concentration in g/mL and l is the length of the polarimeter tube in decimeters. The rotation of an optically active liquid may be measured for the neat liquid or by dissolving the liquid in a solvent. In the case of a neat liquid, c is equal to the density of the liquid in g/mL.

A commercial polarimeter is illustrated in Figure 1L-1. This polarimeter is accurate to ± 0.1°.

Sample tubes of differing lengths may be used, but the most common is the 1-dm (10-cm) tube. The sodium-vapor light source is placed at the end of the instrument away from the eyepiece. The operator peers through the eyepiece and sees the light from the lamp as it traverses through the sample tube. The field is adjusted by turning the wheel to the right or left until it looks homogeneous as shown in Figure 1L-2. Sample fields in the figure on the left and right are in need of adjustment whereas the field in the center is correct and a rotation reading may be taken without further adjustment.

Optical Purity and Enantiomeric Excess

Impure samples of optically active compounds give calculated specific rotations that are less than the expected specific rotation. Optical purity is the ratio of the specific

Figure 1L-1

Placing a sample tube in a (commercial) polarimeter

© Copyright 1996 by Cole-Palmer Instrument Company; used with permission.

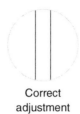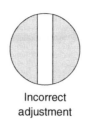

Incorrect   Correct   Incorrect
adjustment   adjustment   adjustment

Figure 1L-2

Polarimeter viewing
field

rotation of the sample over the specific rotation of the pure enantiomer, multiplied by
100%. Optical purity is also equal to the difference between the percentage of the enantiomer in excess and the percentage of the other enantiomer (enantiomeric excess). It
often happens that a sample of one enantiomer is contaminated by the other enantiomer.
For example, pure L-tartaric acid has a specific rotation of +12.7°. Racemic tartaric acid
contains 50% each of the D and L forms and solutions of the racemic form give no optical rotation. If a solution contains 75% of the L form and 25% of the D form, then the
optical purity is equal to 75% – 25% = 50%. Rotation of part of the L form (25%) is
cancelled by an equal amount of the D form. Therefore, only half of the original tartaric
acid sample is causing a rotation. There are two methods of doing the calculation.

Measurement of Optical Rotation and Calculation of Optical Purity

Calculation of optical purity (o.p.) is done by dividing the specific rotation of a mixture
containing an enantiomer by the specific rotation of that enantiomer as in Equation (1.8).

$$\text{o.p.} = \frac{[\alpha]_{\text{impure enantiomer}}}{[\alpha]_{\text{pure enantiomer}}} \times 100\% \qquad (1.8)$$

For example, the observed rotation is + 0.95° for a solution of L-tartaric acid that
has a concentration of 0.15 g/mL using a 1-dm tube. In order to do the calculation from
experimental data, it is necessary to read the experimentally observed rotation and to
calculate the observed specific rotation using Equation (1.7).

$$[\alpha] = \frac{+0.95°}{0.15 \text{ g/mL} \times 1\,\text{dm}} = +6.3°$$

The specific rotation of pure L-tartaric acid is 12.7°. Using Equation (1.8), the optical
purity of the solution is:

$$\text{o. p.} = 6.3°/12.7° \times 100\% = 50\%$$

Calculation of Enantiomeric Excess

In the second method, enantiomeric excess is calculated from the percentages of each
enantiomer in a mixture, if known. The difference between the percentages of the major
(En1) and minor (En2) enantiomers gives the enantiomeric excess (e. e.):

$$\text{e.e.} = \%\text{En1} - \%\text{En2}$$

The solution contained 75% of L-tartaric acid and 25% of D-tartaric acid. Therefore, the enantiomeric excess was 50%:

$$\text{e.e.} = 75\% - 25\% = 50\%$$

It can be seen from these two examples that optical purity is equivalent to enantiomeric excess:

$$\text{optical purity} = \text{enantiomeric excess}$$

How to Measure Optical Rotation

If the sample is a liquid, introduce it directly into the sample tube. If the sample is a solid or a liquid in short supply, weigh the sample and dissolve in a specified volume of solvent, such as water, ethanol, or ethyl acetate. Place the liquid or solution in the sample tube, usually a 1-dm tube, which holds about 10 mL of liquid. Fill the tube completely, as any air bubbles may result in incorrect readings. Place the sample tube in the sample compartment and close the compartment door. If the sample tube area is being adjusted to a temperature other than room temperature, allow the system to achieve temperature equilibration.

Focus the polarimeter. Adjust the field by rotating the inner cylinder holding the eyepiece. **Do not adjust the position of the lamp or the instrument. If either has been moved, notify the instructor.** Rotate the wheel holding the eyepiece slowly to the right. The field appears as shown in Figure 1L-2. When the field is adjusted correctly to take a reading, both the outer fields and the inner field should have matching shades. If no match is found initially, try rotating the inner wheel to the left and look for matching fields. When a match is found, read the scale. Refer to Figure 1L-3 for a view of the scale.

Miniscale

Repeat the process on the same sample two or three times. Approach the desired field from opposite directions and take an average of the readings. The averaged reading should be accurate to 0.05°. Repeat using 20 mL of the same solution in the 2-dm

Figure 1L-3

Polarimetry scale

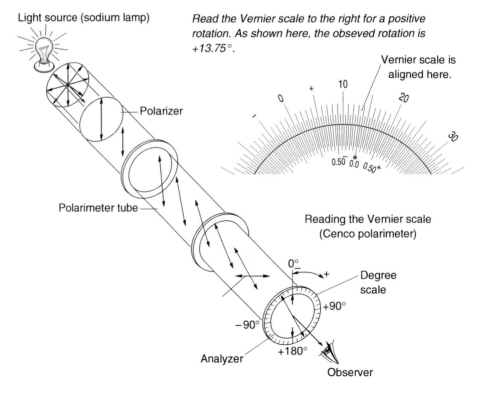

Light source (sodium lamp)

Polarizer

Polarimeter tube

Analyzer

Observer

Read the Vernier scale to the right for a positive rotation. As shown here, the obseved rotation is +13.75°.

Vernier scale is aligned here.

Reading the Vernier scale
(Cenco polarimeter)

Degree scale

0°

+90°

−90°

+180°

cell. If the first reading was correct, the second reading should be double the first reading. Rinse the polarimeter tubes with pure solvent and place the solution in the appropriate container marked for this purpose. Add pure solvent to one of the tubes and take several readings. If the readings differ from 0.00°, the observed reading for the sample solution should be corrected to account for the difference.

Remove the solvent and place it in a container marked for used solvent. Drain the tube, rinse with solvent and place back in the box. Be careful when leaving a tube unattended on the lab bench. It could accidentally roll off the bench.

Exercise L.1: Determining Optical Purity of an Unknown Liquid

Be certain that the polarimeter shows a reading of zero prior to making measurements. Pipet 10.0 mL of an unknown optically active liquid or solution into a small Erlenmeyer flask. Weigh the liquid and calculate its density. Fill a 10-mL polarimeter tube with the unknown liquid. Measure the optical rotation of the liquid. This is the observed rotation. Rinse out the polarimeter tube using a small amount of acetone. Calculate and record the specific rotation of the unknown liquid and temperature.

Safety First!

Always wear eye protection in the laboratory.

Exercise L.2: Determining the Melting Points of Enantiomers and Racemates

Obtain three samples of unknown solids: two enantiomers and their racemic form. Place a sample of each into separate melting point capillaries and take the approximate melting points. Repeat this process using a slower heating rate. Record the melting points of each solid. Explain the results obtained in the melting point determinations.

Safety First!

Always wear eye protection in the laboratory.

Questions

1. A solution of L-glyceraldehyde (0.25 g/mL) in water has an observed rotation of −2.17° in a 1-dm tube at 20°C using a sodium lamp. Calculate the specific rotation of L-glyceraldehyde.

2. Predict the observed rotation of a 0.100 M aqueous solution of L-tartaric acid measured in a 1-dm tube at 20°C. The specific rotation of L-tartaric acid is +12.7°. The molecular mass of L-tartaric acid is 150.09 g/mole.

3. D-Tartaric acid is available commercially and has a specific rotation of −12.0°. Give a likely reason that the value is not −12.7°.

4. A student's calculation of specific rotation is found to be a factor of 10 too small. Suggest a likely reason for this error.

5. A student obtains an observed optical rotation of = +45.5°. A second student challenges the reading and says that it should really be −314.5°. Which student is correct? How can the dispute be settled by using another measurement?

6. A solution is found to have an enantiomeric excess of 10% of the D enantiomer of a substance. How much of the D form is present and how much of the L form is present?

7. A student is asked to prepare 10 mL of a 1.0 M solution of a compound (MW = 100) that is 60% optically pure, starting with the pure enantiomers and solvent. Describe what should be done.

8. D-Tartaric acid has a specific rotation recorded in common handbooks, but (+,–)-tartaric acid has no reported specific rotation. Why?

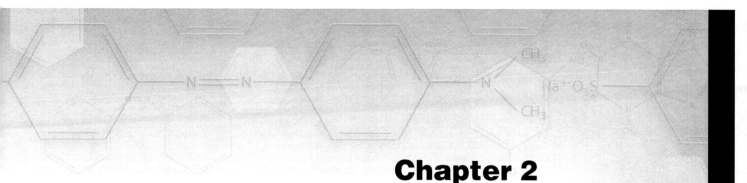

Chapter 2

Spectroscopic Methods and Molecular Modeling

S pectroscopy has revolutionized the world of organic chemistry. Infrared (IR) spectroscopy is now practiced in most laboratories and students can use IR spectrophotometers to record and interpret an IR spectrum. The use of IR spectroscopy and an introduction to interpretation of spectra are described in Technique M.

Nuclear magnetic resonance (NMR) spectroscopy is covered extensively in organic chemistry texts. This is a very powerful tool for elucidating structures of organic compounds. The identities of many simple organic compounds can be deduced from their NMR spectra alone. For time spent, NMR spectroscopy gives the most useful information about structure. Two types of NMR spectroscopy are discussed in Technique N. One is proton NMR spectroscopy and the other is carbon NMR spectroscopy. Recording of spectra is included in the exercises if equipment is available. If not, it is still possible to do the spectral exercises that are included.

Ultraviolet (UV) spectroscopy has limited use in the organic chemistry laboratory. However, there are some advanced, specific applications where UV spectroscopy is the only technique that gives the structural information required. Compounds containing alternating single and double bonds (conjugated) give measurable UV spectra. If the conjugation is very extensive and the compound is colored, visible spectroscopy can be used as an analytical method. UV spectroscopy and visible spectroscopy are described in Technique O. They are used to study reaction rates in this text.

Mass spectrometry (MS), which is covered in Technique P, has seen increased use in many undergraduate laboratories because of greater availability of instrumentation. The combination of gas chromatography and MS in the same instrument (GC/MS) is the most available and most easily operated MS instrument for organic chemistry students. MS gives important information about molecular weight and the complexities of molecules. MS can be used in combination with other spectroscopic methods to elucidate structure.

Molecular modeling using molecular modeling kits or molecular modeling computer software is introduced in Technique Q. The advent of modeling software and personal computers capable of running the software programs has created a new technique for organic chemistry. Molecular modeling is introduced as a technique in this chapter and is applied in several experiments in this book.

Technique M: Infrared Spectroscopy

Theory

When an organic molecule absorbs radiant energy, vibrations of certain bonds within the molecule become excited. If the frequency of incident radiation matches the specific vibrational frequency of the bond, the bond is excited from a lower vibrational state to a higher vibrational state and the amplitude of the vibration increases. Specific vibrations result from absorption of specific frequencies of infrared radiation. Structurally different molecules do not absorb exactly the same energies of infrared radiation so they give different patterns of absorption. Specific bonds and functional groups in the molecule have specific vibrational frequencies, so they absorb characteristic frequency ranges of radiation.

When infrared radiation is passed through a thin-film or wafer-thin sample, some of the light passes directly through the sample. But certain frequencies corresponding to specific vibrational frequencies within the molecule are absorbed. This makes infrared (IR) spectroscopy a valuable tool for identifying different functional groups.

The two most important vibrational modes in IR spectroscopy are "stretching and bending." These are illustrated for vibrational modes of the methylene ($-CH_2-$) group (see Figure 2M-1).

Stretching involves a change in the interatomic distance. Stretching is symmetric if atoms move in opposite directions along the internuclear axis and is asymmetric if the atoms move in the same direction.

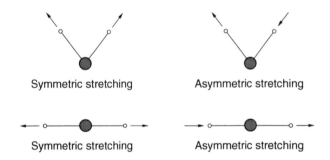

Symmetric stretching   Asymmetric stretching

Symmetric stretching   Asymmetric stretching

For bending, IR absorption causes a change in bond angles. Types of bending modes include scissoring, rocking, wagging, and twisting. Stretching requires more energy than bending, so it occurs at higher frequencies (shorter wavelengths). Asymmetric stretching requires more energy than symmetric stretching.

Stretching and bending must cause a change in the dipole moment of the bond in order to be IR active. Bonds that show large changes in bond dipole moment give more intense IR absorption than bonds that show small changes in bond moment. For example, IR absorption due to carbon-oxygen double bond stretching is intense, but absorption due to carbon-carbon double bond stretching is weak. IR absorption by the polar carbon-oxygen bonds leads to a change in dipole moment and therefore results in intense peaks.

An IR spectrum is a graph of absorption intensity (given as percent transmittance) as a function of radiation frequency (given as wavenumber in units of reciprocal centimeters—cm^{-1}). Frequency and wavenumber are directly proportional; therefore, wavenumber is also directly proportional to energy: the higher the wavenumber, the greater the energy. The range of the wavenumber scale is 4000 to 600 cm^{-1}. IR spectra may also display a wavelength scale, in microns (μ). The range of wavelengths is 2.5 to 16 μ.

$$E = h\nu = \frac{hc}{\lambda}$$

STRETCHING   BENDING

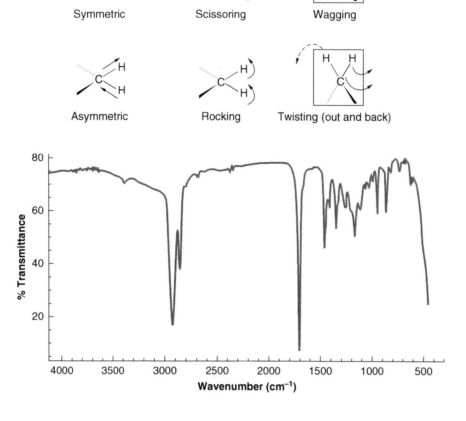

Figure 2M-1

Stretching and bending modes of a methylene ($-CH_2-$) group

Figure 2M-2

IR spectrum of cycloheptanone (neat)

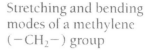

The IR spectrum of cycloheptanone is shown in Figure 2M-2. Absorptions are shown as "valleys," some of which are broader than others. IR absorptions are broadened due to the number of rotational energy states available to each vibrational state.

Bonds give rise to characteristic IR absorption frequencies and intensities. The energy required to excite a given vibrational mode is dependent upon the size of the atoms and strengths of the bonds. The frequency of absorption is proportional to the square root of the force constant for the bond divided by the reduced mass:

$$\bar{v} = \frac{1}{2\pi c}\sqrt{\frac{k}{\mu}}$$

where $\bar{v}$ is the vibrational frequency, k the force constant and μ the reduced mass $[m_1 m_2/(m_1 + m_2)]$. In general, the smaller the atoms, the better the overlap and the higher the frequency of absorption. As atomic size increases, the frequency decreases. Bond strength also influences the frequency of absorption. This means that a carbon-carbon triple bond vibrates (higher force constant, k) at higher frequencies than a carbon-carbon double bond, which vibrates at higher frequencies than a carbon-carbon single bond:

alkyne	carbon-carbon triple bond stretching	(2250–2100 cm^{-1})
alkene	carbon-carbon double bond stretching	(1680–1600 cm^{-1})
alkane	carbon-carbon single bond stretching	(1200–800 cm^{-1})

Similarly, a carbonyl group (C=O) vibrates at higher energy than does a carbon-oxygen single bond:

$$C=O \qquad (1810\text{–}1630 \text{ cm}^{-1})$$

$$C-O \qquad (1300\text{–}1000 \text{ cm}^{-1})$$

Ranges of absorption do not necessarily imply that there is broad absorption over the entire range. Rather, the maximum absorption may occur anywhere within the range listed. These bond frequencies are used to predict IR absorption frequencies. A compound containing a carbonyl group absorbs IR radiation in the region of 1810–1630 cm^{-1} because the frequency of light matches the vibrational frequency of the carbonyl group.

$$C\equiv C-H \quad 3300 \text{ cm}^{-1}$$
$$C=C-H \quad 3100\text{–}3000 \text{ cm}^{-1}$$
$$C-C-H \quad 3000\text{–}2800 \text{ cm}^{-1}$$

Hybridization affects the characteristic absorption frequency of the carbon-hydrogen bond. The greater the s character, the shorter and stronger the bond. Carbon-hydrogen bonds of sp hybridized carbons are stronger than carbon-hydrogen bonds of sp^2 hybridized carbons, which are stronger than carbon-hydrogen bonds of sp^3 hybridized carbons. Therefore sp C−H stretching occurs at higher frequency than sp^2 C−H stretching and sp^3 C−H stretching.

Conjugation also affects the frequency of absorption. Conjugated alkenes and carbonyl compounds absorb at lower frequencies than their nonconjugated counterparts. The shift is about 30 cm^{-1} per unit of conjugation. Conjugation of a double bond lengthens the bond, reducing the force constant.

Three important regions of the IR spectrum indicating functional groups are the region from 3600–3100 cm^{-1} where OH and NH stretching occur, the region around 1700 cm^{-1} where C=O stretching occurs, and the region around 1650 cm^{-1} where C=C stretching occurs. Many important functional classes, such as alcohols, amines, amides, carboxylic acids, ketones, aldehydes, esters, alkenes, and aromatic compounds are identified by the presence (or absence) of absorption in these regions.

Region from 3650 to 3100 cm⁻¹ (C−H, N−H, OH)

Although both OH and NH stretching occur in this region, they can be distinguished by the intensity of the peaks. Neat liquid samples of alcohols and phenols give one very broad, very intense absorption around 3650–3200 cm^{-1}, while neat liquid samples of amines or amides may show absorption bands around 3550–3100 cm^{-1} that are somewhat sharper and less intense. Primary amines and unsubstituted amides show two bands in this region while secondary amines show only one band. Tertiary amines do not give absorption in this region. Carboxylic acids show strong and extremely broad OH stretching (3300–2400 cm^{-1}), which sometimes obscures the carbon-hydrogen stretching band. It is generally easy to differentiate between an alcohol, an amine, and a carboxylic acid, as illustrated by the spectra shown in Figure 2M-3. Terminal alkenes, aromatic compounds, and alkynes also show absorption in this region. sp^2 C−H stretching for terminal alkenes and aromatic compounds occurs at higher frequencies than sp^3 C−H stretching, around (3100–3000 cm^{-1}), while sp C−H stretching for terminal alkynes occurs at 3300 cm^{-1}.

Region around 1700 cm⁻¹ (C=O)

This is the region that corresponds to carbonyl absorption. The actual absorption frequency depends both upon the type of carbonyl (ketone, aldehyde, ester, amide, anhydride, or acid chloride) and the degree of conjugation. An attached electron-withdrawing substituent raises the energy of absorption and the frequency. Thus, acid chlorides absorb at higher frequencies than do ketones or aldehydes. Amides and carboxylic acids have

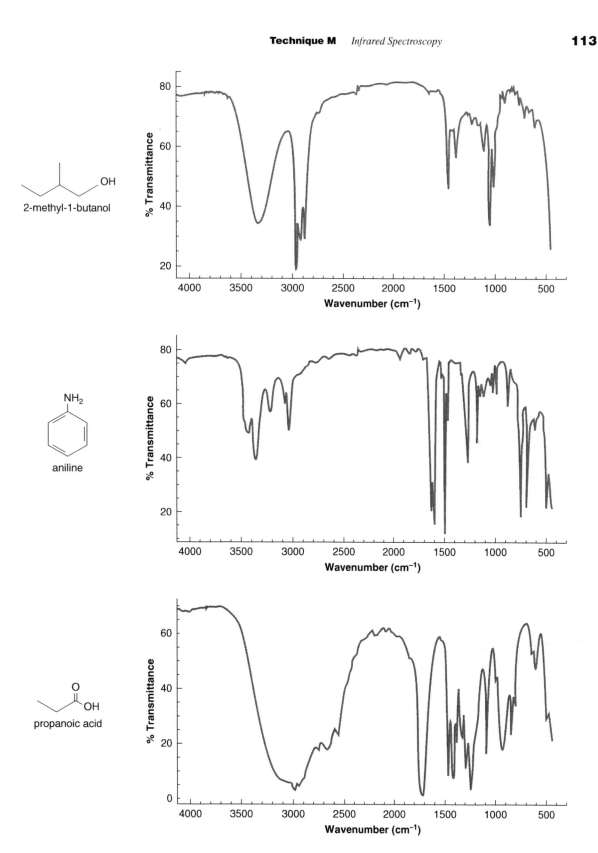

Figure 2M-3 IR spectra of an aliphatic alcohol, a primary aromatic amine, and an aliphatic carboxylic acid (neat liquids)

lower carbonyl absorption frequencies than ketones. In the case of amides, lower absorption frequencies are due to conjugation (resonance). In the case of carboxylic acids, the lowering of energy is due to strong intermolecular hydrogen bonding. This weakens the carbonyl, resulting in a lower energy absorption. This trend in the approximate carbonyl stretching frequency is summarized below for aliphatic carbonyl compounds:

Anhydrides	1810 cm^{-1} and 1760 cm^{-1}	(both very strong)
Acid chlorides	1800 cm^{-1}	(very strong)
Esters	1735 cm^{-1}	(very strong)
Aldehyde	1725 cm^{-1}	(very strong)
Ketone	1715 cm^{-1}	(very strong)
Carboxylic acid	1710 cm^{-1}	(very strong)
Amide	1660 cm^{-1}	(strong)

Conjugation with carbon-carbon double bonds and aromatic rings lowers the absorption frequency. For example, the carbonyl stretching frequency of 3-methyl-2-butanone, an aliphatic ketone, occurs at 1715 cm^{-1}, while the carbonyl stretching frequency of 4-methyl-3-penten-2-one, a conjugated ketone, occurs at 1700 cm^{-1}.

O ← 1715 cm⁻¹   O ← 1700 cm⁻¹

3-methyl-2-butanone   4-methyl-3-penten-2-one

Region around 1600 cm⁻¹ (C=C, C=N)

In this region are carbon-carbon (C=C) stretching of unsymmetrical alkenes and aromatics ($1680–1430 \text{ cm}^{-1}$) and carbon-nitrogen (C=N) stretching ($1690–1500 \text{ cm}^{-1}$). Conjugation lowers the energy of absorption due to a resonance effect.

A summary of important types of bonds and their approximate characteristic absorptions is shown in Figure 2M-4:

Figure 2M-4

Useful characteristic IR bond stretching frequencies

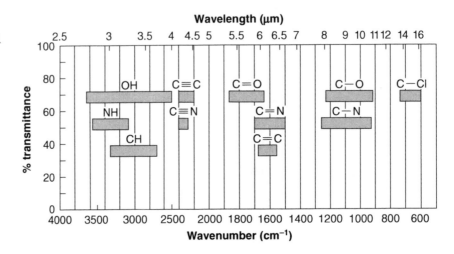

Conjugation and resonance generally decrease absorption frequencies, whereas ring strain increases absorption frequencies and ring strain affects the actual frequency of absorption. The values in the chart in Figure 2M-4 represent ranges. Other functional groups also have characteristic absorption bands. A summary of characteristic absorption bands for various functional groups is given in the correlation chart in Table 2M-1.

Table 2M-1   Absorption Frequencies of Specific Functional Groups

Type of compound	Major IR bands (cm^{-1}) (approximate)	Notes
Alkane	3000 (C–H stretching) 1465 (CH$_2$ scissoring) 1450 (CH$_3$ asymmetric bending) 1375 (CH$_3$ symmetric bending)	Saturated hydrocarbons give simple spectra, with few absorptions. An isopropyl group shows two equally intense peaks around 1385 and 1370 cm^{-1}, while for a *tert*-butyl group, the peaks are of unequal intensity.
Alkene	3100 (**H**–**C**=C stretching) 1630 (weak) (C=C stretching) 1000–650 (**H**–**C**=C out-of-plane bending)	Monosubstituted alkenes show two strong bands at 990 and 910 cm^{-1}. *cis*-Alkenes show one strong band around 700 cm^{-1}, while *trans*-alkenes have one strong band near 890 cm^{-1}. Symmetrical alkenes do not show a C=C stretching absorption.
Alkyne	3300 sharp (**H**–**C**≡C) stretching 2150–2100 (C≡C stretching)	Absorption at 2150–2100 cm^{-1} is weak or absent for internal alkynes.
Aromatic	3100 (sp^2 C–H stretching) 2000–1667 (overtone bands) 1600–1475 (C=C ring stretching) 900–690 (out-of-plane bending)	Bands at 900–690 cm^{-1} show the alkyl substitution pattern: mono-substituted—two bands near 750 and 700 cm^{-1}; *ortho*-disubstituted—one band near 750 cm^{-1}; *meta*-disubstituted—three bands near 890, 800, and 690 cm^{-1}; and *para*-disubstituted—one band near 830 cm^{-1}.
Alkyl halide	800–600 (C–Cl stretching)	C–Br and C–I absorb in the far infrared region (<690 cm^{-1}). Aryl chlorides have C–Cl stretching at 1096–1089 cm^{-1}.
Alcohol and phenol	3650–3200 broad (OH stretching) 1250–1000 (C–O stretching)	Neat alcohols absorb near 3300 cm^{-1}. Broad width of the band is due to intermolecular hydrogen bonding. The position of the C–O stretching band varies for a primary, secondary, and tertiary alcohol: 1050 cm^{-1} (primary); 1100 cm^{-1} (secondary); 1150 cm^{-1} (tertiary). In phenols, this band is around 1220–1200 cm^{-1}.
Ether	1300–1000 (C–O stretching)	For aliphatic ethers, this is generally the main band of interest. Aromatic ethers have two bands at 1245 and 1030 cm^{-1}.
Amine	3550–3250 (N–H stretching) 1640–1560 broad (N–H bending—primary amine) 1250–1000 (C–N stretching)	Primary amines show two overlapping absorption bands at 3550–3250 cm^{-1}, while secondary amines have only one. Tertiary amines do not absorb in this region. Aliphatic amines also show weak to moderate C–N stretching at 1100–1000 cm^{-1}. This band is shifted to higher frequencies in aromatic amines (1200–1100 cm^{-1}).
Aldehyde	1725 (C=O stretching) 2750 and 2850 (aldehydic C–H stretching)	Carbonyl stretching for aromatic aldehydes is at lower frequency. Bands at 2750 and 2850 cm^{-1} are sharp, but weak. The higher frequency band may be obscured by aliphatic C–H stretching band.
Ketone	1715 (C=O stretching)	Conjugation decreases the frequency of the carbonyl stretching. Strained cyclic ketones absorb at higher frequencies than nonstrained cyclic ketones (1775–1740 cm^{-1}).
Ester	1735 (C=O stretching) 1300–1000 (C–O stretching)	C–O stretching at 1300–1000 cm^{-1} is actually two bands, one stronger than the other. Small ring lactones have higher carbonyl stretching frequencies.
Carboxylic acid	3300–2400 (O–H stretching) 1710 (C=O stretching) 1320–1210 (C–O stretching)	Carboxylic acids have very broad O–H stretching that may obscure the C–H stretching band. The carbonyl stretching is also broad. The carbonyl group in dimerized saturated aliphatic acids absorbs in the region 1720–1706 cm^{-1} while monomeric aliphatic acids show carbonyl absorption near 1710 cm^{-1}.

continued

Table 2M-1 *continued*

Type of compound	Major IR bands (cm^{-1}) (approximate)	Notes
Amide	3550–3060 (N$-$H stretching) 1650 (C$=$O stretching) 1640–1550 (N$-$H bending)	Unsubstituted amides show two N$-$H stretching bands, while mono-substituted amides show one. Disubstituted amides do not absorb in the N$-$H stretching region. The carbonyl stretching frequency is decreased due to resonance.
Anhydride	1810 and 1760 (two C$=$O stretches) 1300–900 (C$-$O stretching)	Anhydrides give two strong carbonyl bands, one for symmetric stretching and the other for asymmetric stretching.
Nitrile	2260–2240 (C$\equiv$N stretching)	Conjugation decreases the frequency to 2240–2222 cm^{-1}.
Nitro	1550 and 1350 (NO$_2$ stretching)	Symmetric and asymmetric NO$_2$ stretching.

General Approach to Solving an IR Spectrum

IR spectroscopy can be used to identify bond types and functional groups present and bond types and functional groups that are absent. In analyzing an IR spectrum, you should not attempt to identify all of the bands, but look for significant peaks that help you identify functional groups.

A general approach to use is to first look in the region around 1700 cm^{-1} for the presence of carbonyl absorption. If carbonyl absorption is present, note the wavenumber and look for evidence of an aldehyde, ester, carboxylic acid, amide, or anhydride. If there is none, the compound is a ketone. Examine the specified regions for aromaticity and determine if the compound is aromatic or aliphatic. Aromatic compounds and vinylic compounds show sp^2 C$-$H stretching at 3100 cm^{-1}; unsymmetrical alkenes also show C$=$C stretching at 1660–1600 cm^{-1}, and aromatic compounds have two absorptions at 1600 and 1475 cm^{-1}. Aromatics also have strong out-of-plane bending at 900–690 cm^{-1}, characteristic of the substitution pattern. If carbonyl absorption is not present, look at the region 3650–3100 cm^{-1} to see if the molecule contains an OH or NH group or if the compound is an alkene or terminal alkyne. This approach is illustrated in the flow scheme in Figure 2M-5.

Once a functional group has been tentatively identified, you should look for confirmatory absorptions. For example, alcohols show broad OH absorption around 3600 cm^{-1}, but will also show strong C$-$O absorption in the region of 1260–1000 cm^{-1}. The presence of this latter band confirms the identification of the compound as an alcohol. Terminal alkynes show sp C$-$H stretching at 3300 cm^{-1}, but also show a sharp peak at 2150 cm^{-1}. This latter peak is often the most distinctive peak in the IR spectrum of a terminal alkyne because there are few other absorptions in this region. Other functional groups have similar characteristic absorptions. Consult Table 2M-1 for a detailed description.

You should be careful when trying to distinguish between alkanes, alkyl halides, and internal alkynes and alkenes using IR spectroscopy alone. Other spectroscopic methods, simple chemical tests, or analysis of physical properties may be useful in these cases.

Recording an IR Spectrum

In order to record an IR spectrum of a neat liquid, you will need (1) the infrared spectrophotometer, (2) salt plates and holder or an IR card, and (3) the sample. For a solid sample, you will need a mortar and pestle and Nujol oil (to prepare a Nujol mull) or high-quality, dry KBr and a pellet press. Solids may also be dissolved in a volatile solvent and the solution applied to an IR card.

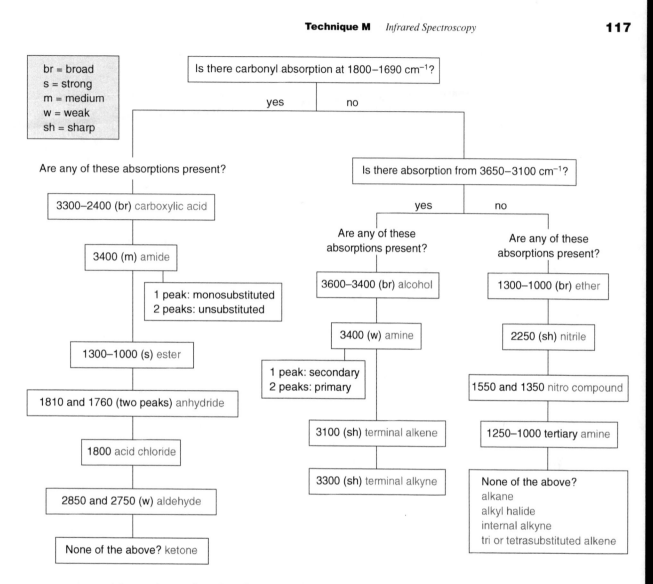

Figure 2M-5 Flow scheme for classifying monofunctional aliphatic compounds using IR spectroscopy

The IR Spectrophotometer

There are two types of IR spectrophotometers, which differ in the mode of radiation. A dispersive IR spectrophotometer contains a prism or grating, which breaks incoming radiation into separate wavelengths. A Fourier transform spectrophotometer (FTIR) provides pulses of radiation containing all wavelengths in the infrared. The two spectrophotometers also differ in schematics.

In a dispersive IR spectrophotometer, a beam of infrared light is split into two beams of equal intensity. The sample cell is in the path of one of the beams; the other goes through a reference cell. The beams pass through a monochromator that systematically varies the wavelength. A detector measures the difference in intensities of absorption between the reference and the sample. The chart recorder measures the difference in intensity as a function of wavenumber (or frequency) as the pen tracks the frequencies from 4000 to 600 cm^{-1} over a period of a few minutes.

In Fourier transform infrared spectroscopy, the entire spectrum is recorded at once and stored in computer memory. The data undergoes a mathematical Fourier transform to convert it to useful data in the normal format. The spectrum can be compared with other spectra stored in memory. For example, a spectrum of an organic sample in methylene chloride solvent can be placed in memory and a prerecorded spectrum of methylene chloride only can be used to subtract the solvent spectrum from that of the sample. The subtraction is generally not perfect, however. For further information about FTIR, see the references at the end of Technique M. All IR spectra in this book are FTIR spectra.

Salt Plates

Salt plates are plates made of large crystals of sodium chloride. Because salt dissolves in water, it is absolutely critical that no water come in contact with the plates, ever! Even the slightest bit of moisture in the sample or on your fingertips is enough to cause pits on the surface of the plate. Handle the salt plates only on the edges. Store them in a desiccator whenever they are not in use.

Salt plates should be cleaned with a few drops of an anhydrous solvent such as methylene chloride or 1,1,2-trichloroethane. Acetone is not a good solvent for cleaning, because it absorbs too much water, which then dissolves the salt plate. To clean the plates, place a few drops of methylene chloride in the middle of each plate. Rub gently with a tissue. Replace in the desiccator when finished.

Hood!

Disposable Cards for IR Spectroscopy

Disposable polyethylene film cards may also be used to obtain spectra of organic compounds. A drop of solution containing an organic sample is applied to the film. The solvent evaporates, producing a very thin film of the organic compound embedded on the polyethylene. These cards are relatively expensive, but they are particularly useful for obtaining IR spectra of solids.

How to Prepare a Sample for IR Analysis

Preparing a Liquid Sample

Take the salt plates from the desiccator and place on a Kim-wipe tissue to avoid scratching the surfaces. With a clean pipet, deposit a drop of the neat liquid (or more, if the liquid is extremely volatile) onto the center of one of the plates. Be certain that the sample is dry and contains no water! Position the other plate directly on top. The liquid will be compressed to a fine film. Make certain there are no air bubbles between the plates. Insert the plates into the cell plate holder. On opposite corners, carefully tighten the bolts. Do not overtighten. The plates are fragile and break easily! Place the cell in the sample side of the spectrometer. Air is the reference.

Preparing a Solid Sample

You can prepare solid samples either using a Nujol mull or by making a KBr pellet. To make a Nujol mull, grind about 10–20 mg of the solid with a mortar and pestle. When the sample is finely ground, add 1–2 drops of Nujol (mineral oil). Grind the sample and Nujol together to make a fine homogenous paste. Spread a dab of the paste on the salt plate, and cover with the second salt plate. The paste should spread evenly between the plates. Make certain there are no air bubbles. Insert the plates into the cell plate holder. On opposite corners, carefully tighten the bolts (Figure 2M-6). Do not overtighten. The plates are fragile and break easily! If the paste is too thick, light cannot get through the

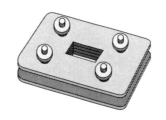

Figure 2M-6

Salt plates and holder

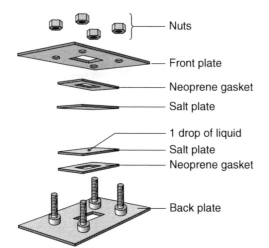

Nuts

Front plate

Neoprene gasket

Salt plate

1 drop of liquid

Salt plate

Neoprene gasket

Back plate

Assembled cell

sample. If this happens, add a little more oil to the mull and mix again. If the paste is too thin, the mull will consist primarily of the Nujol and the IR spectrum of the compound will be weak. If this happens, redo the mull with a higher proportion of compound. Don't forget to subtract out the absorptions due to the Nujol. It is helpful to run a spectrum of pure Nujol to see exactly where the Nujol absorption bands are. Characteristic peaks occur at 2924 cm^{-1}, 1462 cm^{-1}, and 1377 cm^{-1}. The IR spectra of Nujol and acetanilide run as a Nujol mull are shown in Figure 2M-7.

Solid samples can also be run using a KBr pellet. See Figure 2M-8. The KBr must be of extremely high quality and must be extremely dry. It is usually stored in an oven. The handheld or nut/bolt pellet press must also be clean and dry. To make a KBr pellet with the nut/bolt press, insert one bolt into the press so that it goes halfway up into the press. Into the opening put 1–2 mg of the solid and about 100 mg of the finely powdered KBr, which have been previously ground together with a mortar and pestle. Shake the press so that the powder forms a thin, even layer across the bottom. Insert the other bolt and gently tighten. With more force, tighten the bolt, first using hands, and then a wrench. An automotive torque wrench can be used to tighten properly. Do not strip the bolts, but apply enough force so that the sample forms a thin pellet. Then remove both of the bolts. The pellet remains in the press. Carefully examine the pellet. The pellet should be transparent. If it is too thick, light will not be able to get through the sample. If this is the case, remove the pellet and remake it, using slightly less KBr and more force. When an acceptable pellet is formed, place the entire pellet in the holder.

Preparing a Film Card for IR

Although the cost of film cards is prohibitive for large classes, these disposable cards are particularly useful for solid samples. Dissolve 10–20 mg of the solid in a few drops of a volatile solvent in which the solid is soluble. Apply a drop of the solution to the polyethylene film card and allow the solvent to evaporate. Place the card in the holder and record the spectrum. Peaks at 2928, 2850, 1478, and 743 cm^{-1} are due to the polyethylene film. Figure 2M-9 shows the film card and the FTIR spectrum of polyethylene.

The film cards may also be used for nonvolatile liquid samples. Dissolve a drop of liquid sample in a few drops of a volatile solvent, such as diethyl ether or methylene chloride. Apply the solution to the polyethylene film card and allow the solvent to evaporate.

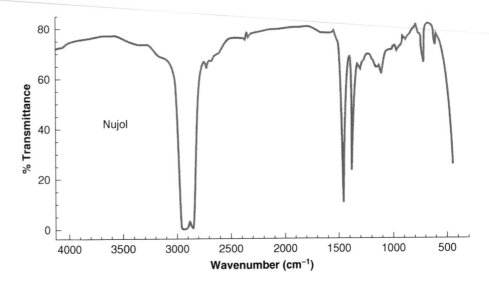

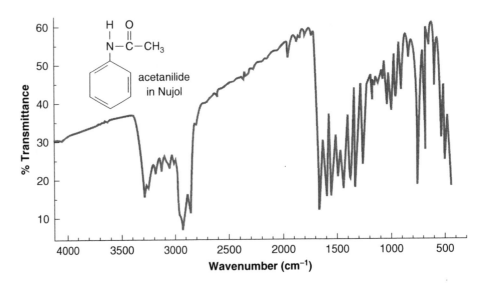

Figure 2M-7   FTIR spectra of Nujol and acetanilide prepared as a Nujol mull

Important Tips Concerning IR

1. Store the recorder pen capped or in a humidifier to keep the ink flowing properly.
2. Store the salt plates in a desiccator to keep water away.
3. Never put a sample that contains water on salt plates.
4. If the peaks are too large and bottom out on the page using dispersive IR spectroscopy, make sure that the Baseline/Offset is set to 90%. Try adjusting the gain. Lower numbers should decrease the amplitude. Try running the spectrum using a smaller amount of sample.

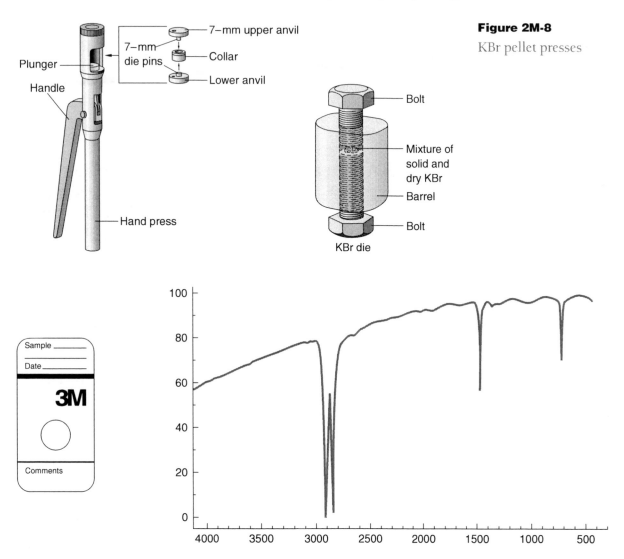

Figure 2M-8

KBr pellet presses

Figure 2M-9   Polyethylene film card and IR spectrum of polyethylene

5. If the peaks are too small, there is not enough sample. Increase the gain. If this is not successful, add more drops of the sample if running a neat liquid. If making a KBr pellet, add more of the sample to the press.

6. If a Nujol mull of a functional compound shows only C−H stretching around 3000 cm^{-1} and two other bands around 1500 and 1400 cm^{-1}, there is too much Nujol and not enough compound. Remake the mull, adding more of the compound.

7. Dispersive-IR spectrophotometers can give inaccurate wavenumbers because of mechanical slippage or paper misalignment and must be calibrated by comparison with reference peaks. To calibrate the instrument, record the IR spectrum of a sample such as polystyrene, which is readily available as a thin transparent film. Polystyrene has a strong absorption at 1601 cm^{-1} that can be used as a reference peak. If the position of this band differs from 1601 cm^{-1}, a correction factor must be applied to the reported wavenumbers of the sample. FTIR instruments do not need to be calibrated.

Exercise M.1: Recording the IR Spectrum of an Organic Liquid

Obtain an organic liquid. Draw the structure of the assigned compound. Obtain an IR spectrum and interpret the major absorption frequencies, using Table 2M-1 of characteristic frequencies.

Exercise M.2: Recording the IR Spectrum of an Organic Solid

Obtain an organic solid. Draw the structure of the assigned compound. Prepare a Nujol mull, a KBr pellet, or an IR card of the solid and obtain an IR spectrum. Interpret the major absorption frequencies, using Table 2M-1 of characteristic frequencies. If a Nujol mull is used, identify the frequencies associated with the mull.

Exercise M.3: Spectroscopic Identification of Unknowns

Look up the structures of the compounds given below. The instructor will assign one or more of the IR spectra, numbered A–F. Identify as many peaks as possible for each spectrum. Then determine the structure of the unknown, which will be one of the following compounds:

acetic anhydride	chlorobenzene	1-octene
allyl alcohol	cyclohexane	2-pentanone
aniline	diethylamine	propanoic acid
anisole	N, N-dimethylformamide	pyridine
benzaldehyde	ethyl benzoate	salicylaldehyde
benzonitrile	ethyl propanoate	styrene
benzyl alcohol	heptane	toluene
benzyl chloride	2-methyl-1-butanol	triethylamine

Questions (continued on p. 125)

1. Which absorbs at higher frequencies: a C−H or C−D bond? Explain.
2. Why does H_2 not give an IR spectrum?
3. Is 2,3-dimethyl-2-butene expected to show a C=C stretching absorption? Explain.
4. How can cyclohexane and 2,2-dimethylpropane be differentiated using IR spectroscopy?
5. Explain why the C=C stretch for a *trans*-disubstituted alkene is weaker than for a *cis*-disubstituted alkene.
6. Explain why primary amines and unsubstituted amides have two NH stretching absorptions.
7. Why do anhydrides show two carbonyl peaks?
8. Why is the carbonyl band in carboxylate salts shifted to frequencies below 1710 cm^{-1}?

Exercise M.3

Spectrum A
Major peaks (cm⁻¹):
3350, 3101,
1660, 1431,
1138, 1042

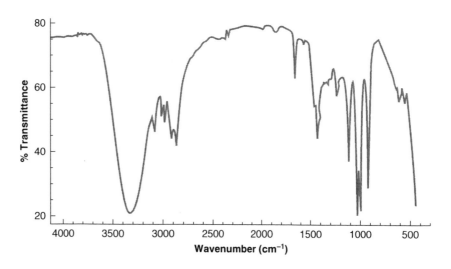

Spectrum B
Major peaks (cm⁻¹):
2980, 1725,
1384, 1175

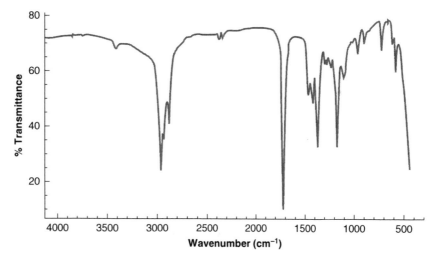

Spectrum C
Major peaks (cm⁻¹):
3044, 2940,
1630, 1516,
758, 700

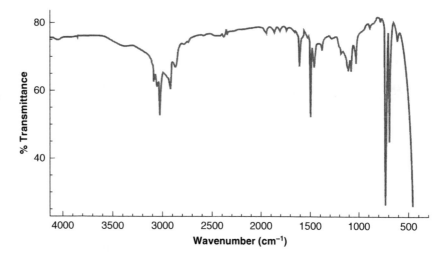

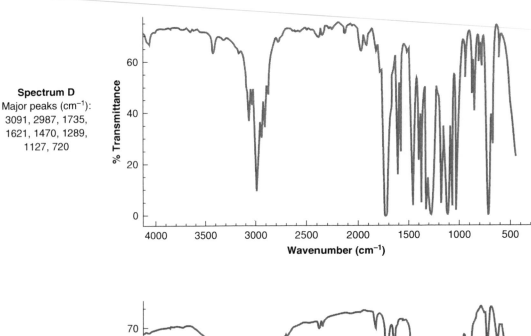

Spectrum D
Major peaks (cm^{-1}):
3091, 2987, 1735,
1621, 1470, 1289,
1127, 720

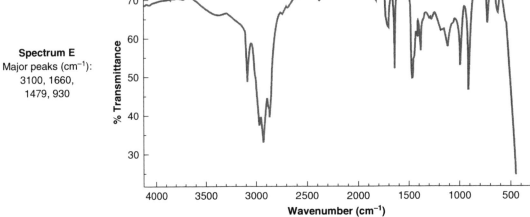

Spectrum E
Major peaks (cm^{-1}):
3100, 1660,
1479, 930

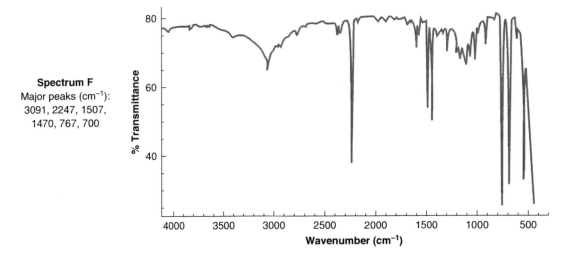

Spectrum F
Major peaks (cm^{-1}):
3091, 2247, 1507,
1470, 767, 700

9. Explain how to distinguish an aliphatic ether from an aromatic ether using IR spectroscopy.
10. Organic liquids must be dried before an IR spectrum is run. Why?
11. Explain how IR spectroscopy can be used to differentiate between an aldehyde, a ketone, and an ester.
12. What identifying features in the IR spectrum help to characterize a tertiary amine?
13. How can *m*-xylene be distinguished from *p*-xylene using IR spectroscopy?
14. How can a nitrile be distinguished from a terminal alkyne in the IR spectrum?
15. Draw the principal resonance forms of 3-buten-2-one. Why does the carbonyl stretching absorption occur at lower frequency than for the carbonyl for acetone?
16. What is Nujol? Explain the IR absorptions given by Nujol.
17. What important factor leads to the strong intensity of carbonyl absorption?

References

Cooper, J. W. *Spectroscopic Techniques for Organic Chemists.* New York: Wiley, 1980.

Kemp, W. *Organic Spectroscopy.* 3d ed. New York: W. H. Freeman and Company, 1991.

Lambert, J. B., Shurvell, H. F., Lightner, D., and Cooks, R. G. *Organic Structural Spectroscopy.* Upper Saddle River, NJ: Prentice-Hall, Inc., 1998.

Pavia, D., Lampman, G., and Kriz, G. *Introduction to Spectroscopy.* 3rd ed. Pacific Grove: Brooks/Cole, 2001.

Silverstein, R. M., Webster, F. X. *Spectrometric Identification of Organic Compounds.* 6th ed. New York: Wiley, 1998.

Technique N: Nuclear Magnetic Resonance Spectroscopy

Introduction

Nuclear magnetic resonance (NMR) spectroscopy is the most important technique for characterization of structure because it reveals specific placement and connectivity of atoms. While infrared (IR) spectroscopy can be used to help determine which functional groups are present in a molecule, NMR spectroscopy can be used to determine the exact location of functional groups. NMR spectroscopy gives valuable information about the carbon skeleton and about the molecule as a whole.

NMR spectroscopy can be applied for any nucleus that has a nuclear spin—that is, any nucleus that has an odd mass number and/or odd atomic number. This includes such nuclei as ^1H, ^{13}C, ^{19}F, ^{15}N, and ^{31}P. ^1H NMR (proton) and ^{13}C NMR are discussed here. For a particular type of atom, such as ^1H, an NMR spectrum shows absorptions, called signals, for each nonequivalent hydrogen: one signal for methane or ethane, two signals for propane or butane, three signals for pentane or hexane, etc. Four valuable types of information may be obtained from a ^1H NMR spectrum:

1. The number of signals in the spectrum indicates the number of nonequivalent protons in the molecule.
2. The position of the signals indicates the magnetic environment of the protons.
3. The intensity of the signals indicates the relative number of protons of each type in the molecule.
4. The splitting of the signal indicates the number of nonequivalent protons on the same or adjacent atoms to the proton being observed.

Theory

To understand the principles behind ^{1}H NMR spectroscopy, it is helpful to think of the nucleus as a tiny bar magnet. When placed in a magnetic field, only two spin states are possible for the hydrogen nucleus. The magnet can be aligned with the magnetic field (spin state = +1/2) or against the field (spin state = –1/2). Since slightly more energy (about 0.0001 calorie more) is required to oppose the magnetic field, there is a slight excess of nuclei aligned with the field (spin state = +1/2). When an electric field is applied at the appropriate radio frequency, these nuclei can absorb energy and "flip" their spins so that their spin now opposes the magnetic field.

How much energy does it take to accomplish this spin flip? The frequency of radiation depends upon the magnetic field strength. For a typical proton, radio-frequency radiation of 300 MHz is needed to reorient spins in a 70,460 Gauss magnetic field. Picture the hydrogen nucleus as being a child's top. The top precesses as it spins in a magnetic field.

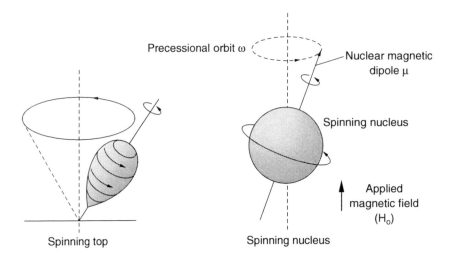

As the magnetic field strength is increased, the angular frequency (ω) increases also. In order to induce a spin flip, the radiation frequency must exactly match the precessional frequency. This condition, called resonance, differs for various protons within the molecule. The exact radio-frequency energy required for resonance of each type of proton depends upon the electronic environment of that proton. When the resonance condition is reached for each type of proton, the detector coil senses absorption of energy and a signal is observed. The number of signals in a ^{1}H NMR spectrum reflects the number of different types of protons in the molecule. The NMR spectrum is a plot of applied magnetic field (H_o) versus signal intensity at a constant radio frequency.

A typical NMR spectrum is shown in Figure 2N-1. The scale on the *x* axis is called the delta (δ) scale. This scale is independent of the type of NMR spectrometer used to record the spectrum:

**Chemical shift:
The difference in
position of the center of
a signal and a reference
signal in ppm.**

$$\text{chemical shift (ppm)} = \frac{\text{shift downfield from TMS (in Hz)}}{\text{spectrometer frequency (in MHz)}}$$

The δ scale on the NMR spectrum in Figure 2N-1 extends from 0 to 10 ppm. This is the range of values in which most protons come into resonance. The strength of the magnetic field increases from left to right. Therefore, going from left to right is considered moving upfield; going from right to left is moving downfield. A higher field strength is required to bring a proton that is upfield into resonance than for a proton that is downfield.

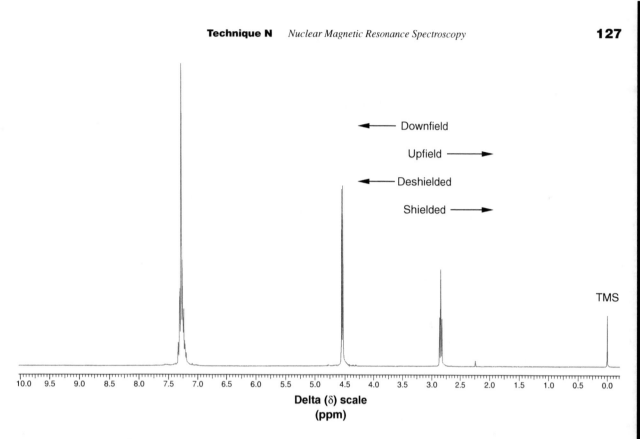

Figure 2N-1   The ^{1}H NMR scale

Source: Reprinted with permission of Aldrich Chemical.

Chemical Shift in ^{1}H NMR Spectroscopy

The positions of the signals give information about the electronic environment of the protons in the molecule. The actual differences between field strengths required to bring individual protons in a molecule into resonance are extremely small—on the order of parts per million (ppm). For this reason, rather than measuring exact field strengths, a process of measuring relative field strengths has been developed. In ^{1}H NMR spectroscopy, the resonance frequency of a known type of proton is used as a reference; the field strengths of all other protons are compared to it. In general, the reference standard used is tetramethylsilane, $(CH_3)_4Si$, more commonly called TMS. This compound is ideal because all of its protons are equivalent and it comes into resonance at higher field strength than most other compounds. A very small amount of TMS is added to a solution of the compound dissolved in a deuterated solvent or other solvent that doesn't contain hydrogens (such as CCl_4). The signal for the TMS is, by definition, at δ0. The field strengths of all the protons in the molecule can be read directly from the spectrum. A proton giving a signal at δ1.0 has a chemical shift of δ1.0. The chemical shift of a proton in a molecule depends upon its electronic environment. Two factors account for the observed chemical shifts, local diamagnetic shielding and the anisotropic effect.

Local Diamagnetic Shielding and Anisotropic Effect

When placed in an external magnetic field, protons are shielded to a certain extent from the applied magnetic field by valence electrons surrounding the nuclei. The electrons establish a weak field that opposes the applied magnetic field. This is called shielding. Shielding is crucial to the utility of NMR as an analytical method. The extent of shielding is dependent upon the electron density around the proton. A higher applied field is needed to bring strongly shielded protons into resonance, so signals from these protons are observed far upfield. Tetramethylsilane is more highly shielded than most other organic molecules. Alkanes and cycloalkanes have small chemical shifts (signals appear at relatively high field strength) because the protons in these molecules are also strongly shielded.

Electronegative substituents bonded to carbon deshield protons bonded to that carbon by withdrawing electron density from around the protons. Because of the decreased electron density, the induced magnetic field is less and the strength of the applied magnetic field required to bring the proton into resonance is lower at a fixed frequency. These deshielded protons come into resonance at lower field strengths (downfield) in ^{1}H NMR spectroscopy (see Figure 2N-2).

In general, protons bonded to carbons bearing electronegative atoms are shifted downfield. The greater the electronegativity of the attached atom, the further downfield the proton. Therefore, the methyl protons of CH_3F appear further downfield ($\delta 4.3$) than the methyl protons of CH_3Cl ($\delta 3.1$) or CH_3Br ($\delta 2.7$). Similarly, the greater the number of electronegative substituents, the further downfield the proton. Thus, the chemical shifts of the methyl protons increase in this order: CH_3Cl ($\delta 3.1$), CH_2Cl_2 ($\delta 5.35$), $CHCl_3$ ($\delta 7.25$).

The chemical shift of a proton can be used to identify its functionality. Figure 2N-2 shows the correlation of chemical shifts of a variety of protons bonded to different functional groups. Notice that protons bonded to oxygen atoms (alcohols) and protons bonded to nitrogen atoms (amines and amides) come into resonance over a very wide range. The exact chemical shift of these protons will depend upon various factors such as the pH of the solution, the concentration of the solution, the temperature, and the degree of hydrogen bonding within the molecule. A detailed correlation of chemical shift values is given in Table 2N-1 and inside the back cover.

Proximity to an electronegative atom does not explain all of the observed chemical shifts. For example, vinyl protons (those attached to a carbon-carbon double bond) have chemical shifts in the range of $\delta 5$–6. This is significantly further downfield than both aliphatic protons and acetylenic protons (protons bonded to a carbon–carbon triple bond). Aromatic protons come into resonance even farther downfield—around $\delta 7$. Within the molecules, circulating electrons induce a magnetic field that either reinforces the applied field or opposes the applied field, depending upon the geometry of the molecule. This is called an **anisotropic effect.** For alkenyl and aryl protons, the induced field

Figure 2N-2

Relationship between functional group and chemical shift in ^{1}H NMR spectroscopy

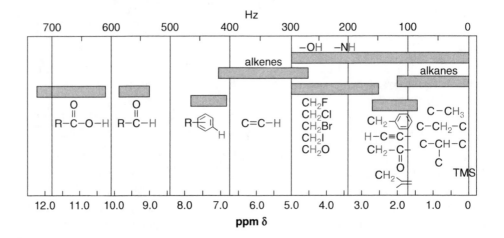

Table 2N-1 ^{1}H NMR Chemical Shift Values for Specific Types of Protons

Type of Proton	Approximate δ Value
Alkane	
methyl ($-CH_3$)	0.9
methylene ($-CH_2^-$), $-CH_2$	1.3
methine ($-CH-$)	1.4
Allyllic: $C=C-CH$	1.6–2.6
Benzylic: $ArC-H$	2–3
α to Carbonyl: $-CO-CH$	2.1–2.5
Alkyne: $RC\equiv CH$	2.5
α to Amines: RCH_2NH_2	2.5–3.0
α to Halide: RCH_2X	3–4
α to Oxygen: RCH_2O-	3–4
Vinyl: $C=C-H$	4.5–6.5
Aromatic: $Ar-H$	6.5–8.5
Aldehyde: $R-CHO$	9–10
Carboxylic acid: RCO_2H	10–12
Alcohols: $RO-H$	Variable: 2–5
Phenols: $ArO-H$	Variable: 4–7

reinforces the applied field and the chemical shifts of these protons are farther downfield. For acetylenic protons, the induced field opposes the applied field; more energy is needed to bring these protons into resonance and their chemical shifts are upfield.

Generally, signals in the chemical shift region of δ7-8 indicate aryl protons and a signal in the region of δ5–6 indicates alkenyl protons. Chemical shift ranges for various types of protons are given in Table 2N-1. Chemical shifts for aromatic protons, alkenyl protons and alkynyl protons result from the positioning of these groups with respect to the applied field. The field detected by the bonded protons may vary according to the region of relative shielding or deshielding as shown.

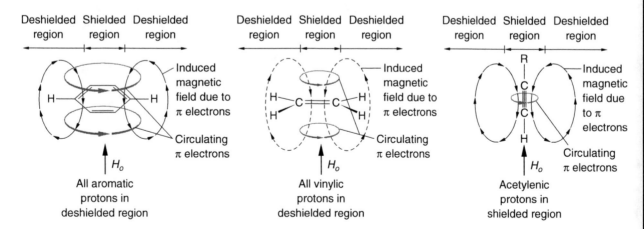

Equivalence of Protons in ^{1}H NMR Spectroscopy

The number of signals in a spectrum is equal to the number of nonequivalent protons in the molecule. Each set of equivalent protons in a molecule gives rise to a signal, the chemical shift of which is dependent upon the electronic environment of the protons.

There are two sets of equivalent protons in butane ($CH_3CH_2CH_2CH_3$): the six equivalent hydrogens on the methyl groups and the four equivalent hydrogens on the two methylene groups. A plane of symmetry divides the molecule into two equal halves. Butane has two ^1H NMR signals.

$$\begin{array}{cc|cc} (a) & (b) & (b) & (a) \\ CH_3-CH_2 & & CH_2-CH_3 \end{array}$$

There are three sets of equivalent protons in pentane ($CH_3CH_2CH_2CH_2CH_3$): the six protons in the two methyl groups are equivalent; the four hydrogens on carbon-2 and carbon-4 are equivalent; and the two hydrogens in the middle, on carbon-3, are equivalent. Each of these sets of protons differs from the others. Pentane shows three ^1H NMR signals.

There are two ways to determine easily whether protons are equivalent. The first is to look for a plane of symmetry in the molecule. The second is to mentally substitute another element such as bromine for one of the hydrogen atoms and then compare the two structures by writing the IUPAC names. If the names are the same, the protons are equivalent; if the names are different, the protons are not equivalent. The structures shown here have, respectively, one, two, three, and four types of equivalent protons. The individual sets of equivalent protons are marked.

all protons   2 types of protons   3 types of protons   4 types of protons
equivalent

Integration in ^1H NMR Spectroscopy

The intensity of an NMR signal is proportional to the number of protons of each type in the molecule. An FT NMR instrument digitally integrates each signal area and provides ratios of hydrogens for each signal. In continuous-wave NMR (CW NMR), the ratios must be determined experimentally by electronically integrating the signals and measuring the heights of the integrals. There are two ways to determine the number of hydrogens under each signal from the measured heights. If the molecular formula is known, add up the heights of all of the integrals, then divide the heights of each of the integrals by the total heights of all the integrals and multiply by the total number of hydrogens in the formula.

$$\frac{\text{height of integral}}{\text{total heights of all integrals}} \times \begin{array}{c}\text{total number}\\\text{of hydrogens}\end{array} = \begin{array}{c}\text{number of hydrogens}\\\text{in signal}\end{array}$$

The number of hydrogens in a signal can be determined from the integrals. Figure 2N-3 shows the spectrum of a compound having the formula $C_4H_{10}O$, which has been both electronically integrated and measured with a ruler. The electronic integration gives ratios of 0.54 and 0.36; measuring the signals with a ruler gives 74 mm and 48 mm. The signals integrate to 6H and 4H, respectively:

Signal a: [74 mm / (74 mm + 48 mm)] × 10H = 6H

Signal b: [48 mm / (74 mm + 48 mm)] × 10H = 4H

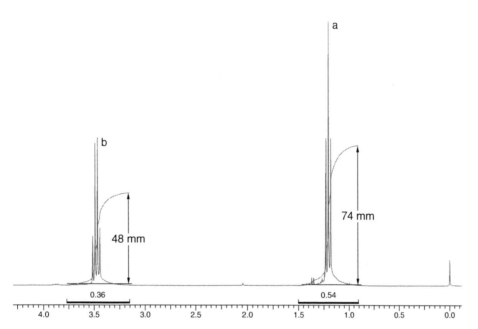

Figure 2N-3

Integrating an NMR spectrum

SOURCE: Reprinted with permission of Aldrich Chemical.

If the formula is not known, integrate by determining the ratio between the signals, rounding off to the nearest whole number or multiplying by a factor to produce a whole number. The electronic integration illustrates this process: signal a = 0.54/0.36 = 1.5; signal b = 0.36/0.36 = 1. The ratio of signal a:b is 1.5H:1H. To get a whole number, multiply by 2. This gives a ratio of signals of 3H:2H. Note that this is just a ratio—without knowing the formula, you can't know the exact number of protons in each signal. For this compound, the actual number of protons under each signal is 6H:4H.

In this book, integrals are generally not plotted so that the nature of each signal can be seen clearly.

Splitting (coupling) in ^{1}H NMR Spectroscopy

Another extremely valuable piece of information can be obtained from an NMR spectrum of a simple organic compound: By evaluating the appearance and number of peaks in each signal, the number of protons on adjacent carbons can be determined. Coupling with nonequivalent protons on adjacent (vicinal) carbon atoms can be observed in ^{1}H NMR spectroscopy. This type of coupling is called "vicinal" coupling. In essence, the protons on a carbon "see" the number of protons on directly adjacent carbon atoms. The number of peaks in a signal equals the number of nonequivalent protons on adjacent carbons (n) plus one more. This is called the "n + 1" rule of spin multiplicity. It applies to cases where vicinal coupling is expected. Magnetically (chemically) equivalent protons do not show spin-spin splitting. For example, in ethane, cyclobutane, and benzene, all of the protons in the molecule are equivalent. In each of these molecules, all protons are equivalent due to symmetry within the molecule.

CH_3CH_3

ethane

cyclobutane

benzene

```
            1
          1   1
        1   2   1
      1   3   3   1
    1   4   6   4   1
  1   5  10  10   5   1
```

Pascal's Triangle

If hydrogens on adjacent carbons are not equivalent, characteristic splitting patterns will be observed. The "n + 1" rule is based on counting the number of nonequivalent protons on directly adjacent carbons to which the proton is coupled and adding one to this number. If there are no nonequivalent protons on directly adjacent carbons, the signal will consist of only one peak (a singlet). With only one nonequivalent proton on adjacent carbons, the signal will be split into two peaks (a doublet); with two nonequivalent protons on adjacent carbons, the signal will be split into three peaks (a triplet); with three, the signal will be split into four peaks (a quartet); with four, the signal will be split into five peaks (a quintet); and with five, the signal will be split into six peaks (a sextet). The number of peaks in a signal and the relative areas of the peaks can be predicted using Pascal's Triangle. Usually anything greater than six peaks is called a multiplet. Since the outermost peaks may shrink into the baseline, it is sometimes difficult to determine the exact number of peaks in a multiplet. Abbreviations are frequently used to describe the peaks, such as "s" for singlet, "d" for doublet, "t" for triplet, "q" for quartet, and "m" for multiplet.

Succinic acid has the structure shown below. The spectrum of succinic acid shows two singlets. The CH_2 groups do not show splitting because the hydrogens are equivalent.

$$H-O-\underset{b}{\overset{\overset{O}{\overset{\|}{C}}}{C}}-\underset{a}{CH_2}-\underset{a}{CH_2}-\underset{b}{\overset{\overset{O}{\overset{\|}{C}}}{C}}-O-H$$

succinic acid

Butane has two types of hydrogens, labeled "a" and "b." Hydrogens "a" are coupled with hydrogens "b." The signal for protons "a" shows a triplet (n + 1 = 2 + 1 = 3). Hydrogens "b" will also be coupled with hydrogens "a," but will not be coupled with each other since they are equivalent. Therefore the signal for "b" will be a quartet (n + 1 = 3 + 1 = 4).

$$\underset{a}{CH_3}-\underset{b}{CH_2}-\underset{b}{CH_2}-\underset{a}{CH_3}$$

butane

When nonequivalent adjacent carbons each have attached protons, spin-spin splitting is usually observed. This arises because the magnetic field experienced by the proton is increased or decreased by the spin state of a neighboring proton. The field experienced by the proton is slightly increased if the neighboring proton is aligned with the field and is decreased if the neighboring proton is aligned against the field. For a single adjacent proton, there are only two possible spin states. This would result in the signal H_a being split into two equal-sized peaks (a doublet) (see Figure 2N-4).

For a proton with two neighboring nonequivalent protons, there are three possibilities: (1) the neighboring protons may have both spins aligned with the field; (2) the neighboring protons may have one spin aligned with the field and one against the field (two possibilities); or (3) both neighboring protons may have their spins aligned against the field. The signal H_a will be split into a triplet, with the middle peak twice as large as the others. Since there is twice the probability that the two neighboring protons will have opposite spins, the middle peak will be twice as large as the outer peaks (Figure 2N-5).

For a proton with three neighboring nonequivalent protons, there are four possibilities: (1) all of the spins may be aligned with the field; (2) two of the spins may be aligned with the field with one spin aligned against the field (three different possibilities); (3) one of the spins may be aligned with the field and two of the spins may be aligned against the field (three different possibilities); and (4) all of the spins may be aligned against the field. This peak will be split into a quartet, with the middle two peaks approximately three times larger than the outer peaks (Figure 2N-6).

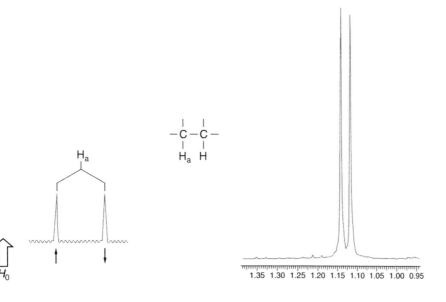

Figure 2N-4

Signal split into a dou-
blet by one adjacent
proton

SOURCE: Reprinted with permission of Aldrich Chemical.

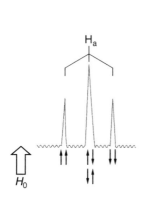

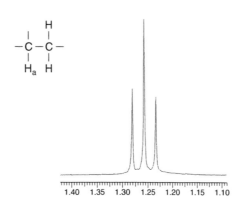

Figure 2N-5

Signal split into a
triplet by two adjacent
protons

SOURCE: Reprinted with permission of Aldrich Chemical.

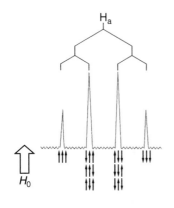

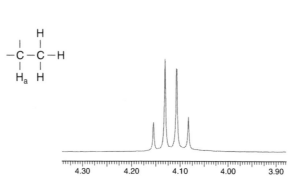

Figure 2N-6

Signal split into quartet
by three adjacent
protons

SOURCE: Reprinted with permission of Aldrich Chemical.

Some typical splitting patterns are illustrated in the NMR spectrum of ethyl acetate in Figure 2N-7.

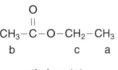

ethyl acetate

Figure 2N-7

^{1}H NMR spectrum of ethyl acetate

SOURCE: Reprinted with permission of Aldrich Chemical.

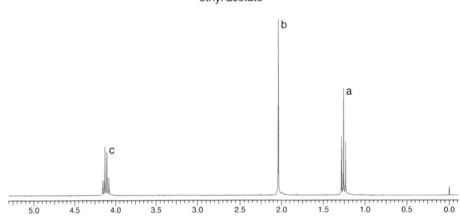

Coupling Constants

The strength of the spin-spin interaction between protons can be determined by measuring the distance between the peaks in a signal. This value, given the symbol J, is called the coupling constant. The J value is independent of field strength. Protons that are more strongly coupled have large J values (expressed in Hertz). For alkanes, J values for vicinal coupling are usually on the order of 7–8 Hz.

The situation is quite different for terminal alkenes. Here coupling can occur between protons on the same carbon (called geminal coupling) in addition to vicinal coupling. For vinyl protons, the coupling constant depends upon the relative position of the protons on the carbon–carbon double bond. Trans coupling constants (J_{trans}) are 12–23 Hz; cis coupling constants (J_{cis}) are around 5–12 Hz; and geminal coupling constants (J_{gem}) are 0–2 Hz. It is usually possible to differentiate between cis and trans protons by measuring the coupling constants. For example, the alkene regions of *cis*-3-chloropropenoic acid and *trans*-3-chloropropenoic acid are shown in Figure 2N-8. Notice that the coupling between protons H$_a$ and H$_b$ is smaller in *cis*-3-chloropropenoic acid than in *trans*-3-chloropropenoic acid. The structures of *cis*-3-chloropropenoic acid and *trans*-3-chloropropenoic acid are shown below:

cis-3-chloropropenoic acid   *trans*-3-chloropropenoic acid

The acidic proton H$_c$ comes into resonance around δ12, and is not shown in either spectrum.

The magnitude of the coupling constant falls off dramatically with increasing distance. Splitting is observed for protons on the same carbon (if the protons are not equivalent) or for protons on adjacent carbons, unless carbon-carbon double bonds are present. For example, anisole has three sets of nonequivalent aromatic protons. Coupling of hydrogens on adjacent carbons, such as H$_a$−H$_b$ (ortho coupling), is 7–8 Hz.

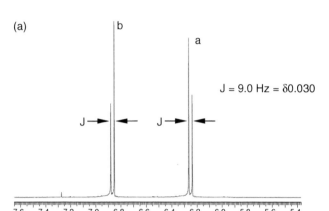

(a)

J = 9.0 Hz = δ0.030

Figure 2N-8

Expanded ^{1}H NMR spectra (alkene protons) of a) *cis*-3-chloropropenoic acid and b) *trans*-3-chloropropenoic acid

SOURCE: Reprinted with permission of Aldrich Chemical

(b)

J = 13.5 Hz = δ0.057

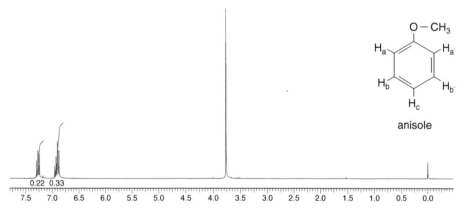

Figure 2N-9

^{1}H NMR spectrum of anisole

SOURCE: Reprinted with permission of Aldrich Chemical.

anisole

0.22 0.33

Coupling for H_a–H_c (meta coupling) is about 3 Hz. Coupling is observed even though H_a and H_c are not on adjacent carbons. This effect is ascribed to conjugation of electron density through π orbitals. Coupling between H_a and $H_{b'}$ (para coupling) is small, but finite (J = 0–1 Hz). The NMR spectrum of anisole is shown in Figure 2N-9.

Protons in a Chiral Environment

There are two signals in the ^{1}H NMR spectrum of chloroethane. The methyl protons are each equivalent and are called homotopic. The methylene protons are equivalent in CDCl$_3$ solution and are called enantiotopic. The distinction between homotopic

CH_3CH_2Cl
chloroethane

Figure 2N-10

^{1}H NMR spectrum of (R)-(-)-2-methyl-2,4-pentanediol

SOURCE: Reprinted with permission of Aldrich Chemical.

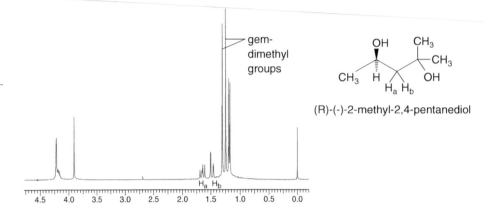

(R)-(-)-2-methyl-2,4-pentanediol

and enantiotopic is that enantiotopic protons are nonequivalent in a chiral environment. Methylene protons adjacent to a stereogenic center are called diastereotopic. They are non-equivalent and they can show different NMR signals. In (R)-(-)-2-methyl-2,4-pentanediol, protons H$_a$ and H$_b$ have different chemical shifts because they are in an achiral environment, being adjacent to a stereogenic center. The NMR spectrum of (R)-(-)-2-methyl-2,4-pentanediol, shown in Figure 2N-10, indicates the complexity of diastereotopic protons. Protons H$_a$ and H$_b$ have different chemical shift values at δ1.46 and δ1.62 and also show different splitting patterns, much different than predicted by the n + 1 rule. The gem-dimethyl groups are also not equivalent but are diastereotopic.

Diastereotopic Protons in Alkenes

Frequently NMR spectra are more complicated than predicted based on first-order approximations. For the examples in this section, the "n + 1" rule generally does not apply. Where it does apply, the coupling constants vary for the peaks within a signal. For example, in the spectrum of vinyl bromide, three signals (for the three types of non-equivalent protons) are expected.

vinyl bromide

Using the "n + 1" rule, H$_c$ should be split into a triplet (since there are two protons on the adjacent carbon); and H$_a$ and H$_b$ should be split into doublets. The actual spectrum of vinyl bromide shows about twelve overlapping peaks. (See Figure 2N-12).

The spectrum of vinyl bromide is complex, because the three vinyl protons are neither chemically equivalent nor magnetically equivalent. To be chemically equivalent all protons must behave identically. To be magnetically equivalent all protons must have the very same chemical shift and be coupled equivalently to all other protons.

In vinyl bromide, protons H$_a$, H$_b$, and H$_c$ are all different. The best way to predict the spectrum of an alkene such as vinyl bromide is with a tree diagram that illustrates the coupling for each proton one at a time. The tree diagram is shown in Figure 2N-11 and the ^{1}H NMR spectrum of vinyl bromide is shown in Figure 2N-12.

H$_c$ will be split into a doublet by H$_a$. The splitting between the peaks will be around 15 Hz. This coupling is labeled J$_{ac}$ to indicate that the coupling is between protons a and c. The next strongest coupling of H$_c$ is with H$_b$; each of the peaks will be further split into a doublet. The distance between these peaks will be around 6 Hz (J$_{bc}$). The signal for H$_c$ will be a doublet of doublets.

For H$_b$, the strongest coupling will be with H$_c$ (cis coupling). H$_b$ will be split into a doublet by H$_c$ with a coupling constant of 6 Hz. Each line will also be split into a doublet by H$_a$, with a coupling constant of around 2 Hz. The signal for H$_b$ will appear as a doublet of doublets. H$_a$ will be split into a doublet by H$_c$ (trans coupling) and into a further doublet by

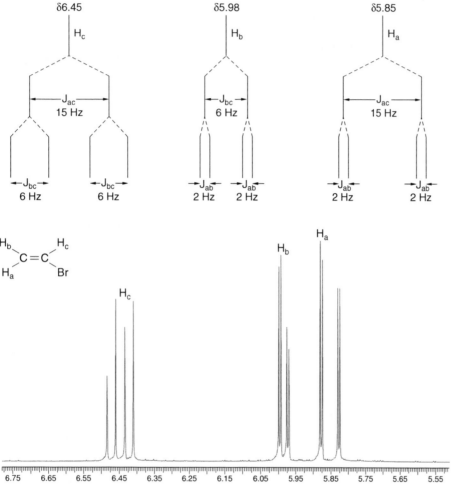

Figure 2N-11

Tree diagram of vinyl bromide

Figure 2N-12

^{1}H NMR spectrum of vinyl bromide

SOURCE: Reprinted with permission of Aldrich Chemical.

H$_b$ (geminal coupling). The signal for H$_a$ will resemble a doublet of doublets. Because the chemical shifts of the protons are so similar, the spectrum appears to be even more complex.

Aromatic compounds, too, show complex splitting due to the magnetic nonequivalence of the protons. In the spectra of some simple alkyl aromatic compounds, such as toluene and ethylbenzene, the signal for all aromatic protons appears to be a singlet. This occurs when the chemical shifts and coupling constants of the protons are very similar. If a splitting pattern is observed, it can yield valuable structural information about the substitution pattern of the aromatic compound. The spectrum for a *para*-disubstituted benzene, in which at least one substituent is not alkyl, commonly appears as an apparent pair of doublets in the region δ7–8. Other substitution patterns give much more complex splitting in this region. The ^{1}H NMR spectra of *p*-bromonitrobenzene and *o*-bromonitrobenzene are shown in Figure 2N-13.

Protons on Heteroatoms

Hydroxyl Protons

Hydroxyl protons (OH) show ^{1}H NMR signals anywhere from δ2 to δ5. The exact chemical shift is concentration dependent. In more concentrated samples, the OH peak is shifted downfield. In more dilute solutions, such as those generally used for 200–300 MHz

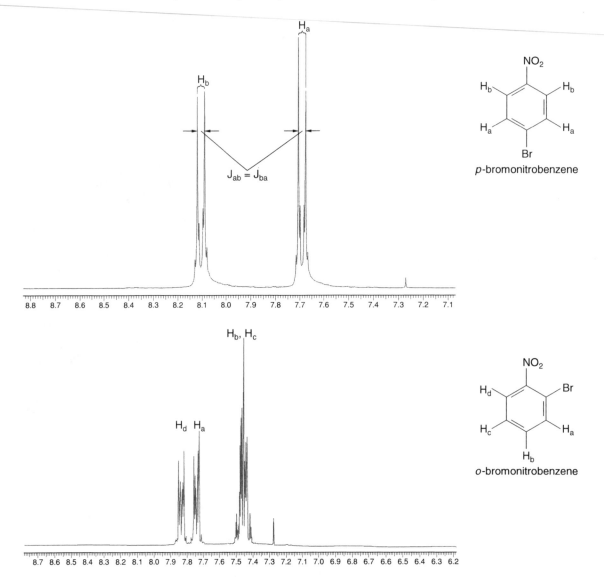

Figure 2N-13   Expanded aromatic regions of *p*-bromonitrobenzene (top) and *o*-bromonitrobenzene (bottom)

SOURCE: Reprinted with permission of Aldrich Chemical.

spectra, the OH signal is observed around δ1–2. The hydroxyl peak for phenols is also concentration dependent, appearing between δ4 and δ7.5. Clearly the chemical shift by itself cannot be used to conclude that the sample is an alcohol or a phenol.

One way to easily identify which peak is due to an OH is to add a drop of D_2O to the sample, shake the tube, and rerun the NMR spectrum. This causes the OH peak to decrease in size or to disappear due to the exchange between the hydrogen and deuterium. (Deuterium has a nuclear spin, but it comes into resonance at different field strengths than protons.)

Coupling may or may not be observed between the hydroxyl proton and other hydrogens on adjacent carbons. If there is rapid exchange of the hydroxylic proton between alcohol molecules, the hydroxyl proton will be a singlet. It is as though the hydroxyl proton weren't on the molecule long enough to couple with hydrogens on adjacent carbons.

There are three conditions under which coupling will be observed: at low temperatures, with extremely pure alcohols, and with dilute solutions. Cooling slows down the rate of exchange, so that under very cold conditions, coupling can be observed. Extremely pure alcohols, which have not even a trace of acid present, will show coupling between hydroxylic protons and hydrogens on adjacent carbons, following the "n + 1" rule. The OH peak for highly purified ethanol is a triplet. However, under room-temperature conditions for alcohols of ordinary purity, the CW NMR spectrum of an alcohol shows a singlet for the hydroxyl proton. For high-field spectra, the OH protons often show coupling because the concentration of sample is very small, limiting hydrogen exchange between OH groups.

Protons on Nitrogen

There are many similarities between the NMR spectra of alcohols and amines. Like protons on oxygen, protons on nitrogen come into resonance anywhere between $\delta 1$ and $\delta 5$. Like alcohols, amines undergo rapid intermolecular exchange, so no splitting is observed between the NH and hydrogens on adjacent carbon atoms in CW NMR spectra. Splitting is usually observed in FT NMR spectra. The amine protons show up typically as a sharp singlet. Protonation of the amine with strong acid (to generate the quaternary ammonium salt) slows the rate of exchange, allowing coupling to be observed. Because nitrogen has a nuclear spin itself, the coupling tends to be complicated.

The NH bond of amides undergoes exchange much more slowly, so coupling between hydrogen on adjacent carbons occurs. However, the NH signal is so broad (due to a phenomenon called "nuclear quadrupole broadening") that splitting may be obscured. Sometimes it is easy to overlook the NH signal of an amide, since it may look like a small "hump" on the baseline. However, integration should still indicate the presence of a hydrogen.

Solvents for ^{1}H NMR Spectroscopy

The most common solvent for NMR spectroscopy is deuterochloroform ($CDCl_3$). Other aprotic solvents can also be used such as deuteroacetone (CD_3COCD_3) and deutero-DMSO (CD_3SOCD_3). Commercially available $CDCl_3$ contains a small amount of $CHCl_3$, which gives a singlet at $\delta 7.2$. Small amounts of water will also appear in the spectrum unless special effort is made to keep the solvent away from water. The chemical shift of the water peak is about $\delta 1.4$ for FT NMR spectra. Similarly, peaks will be seen at $\delta 2.04$ for CHD_2COCD_3 (an impurity in deuteroacetone) and at $\delta 2.49$ for CHD_2SOCD_3 (an impurity in deutero-DMSO). Both signals show closely spaced quintets. Table 2N-2 lists properties of NMR solvents.

Table 2N-2   Properties of NMR Solvents

Deuterated NMR Solvents	Structure	Solvent impurity Chemical shift (δ) and multiplicity	
		^{1}**H NMR**	^{13}**C NMR**
Acetone	CD_3COCD_3	2.04(5)	29.8(7), 206.5(7)
Acetonitrile	CD_3CN	1.93(5)	1.3(7), 118.2(7)
Benzene	C_6D_6	7.24(1)	128.0(3)
Chloroform	$CDCl_3$	7.24(1)	77.5(3)
Deuterium oxide	D_2O	4.63–4.67(1)	—
Dimethyl sulphoxide	CD_3SOCD_3	2.49(5)	39.7(7)
Methyl alcohol	CD_3OD	4.78(1), 3.30(5)	49.0(7)

Solvents used for spectra in this book are $CDCl_3$ and CD_3SOCD_3.

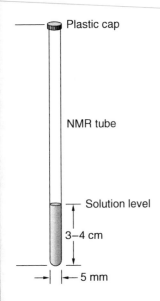

Plastic cap

NMR tube

Solution level

3–4 cm

5 mm

Figure 2N-14

CW NMR tube

How to Prepare a Sample for 60–90 MHz CW ^{1}H NMR Spectroscopy

Wear gloves and work in the hood when preparing solutions for NMR analysis. Prepare solutions that contain about 10 to 15% of the organic solute in the NMR solvent. Measure 40–50 mg of the sample into a small vial. Add 0.4–0.5 mL of the NMR solvent containing TMS with a clean, dry syringe or new Pasteur pipet. Cap and shake the vial to mix thoroughly before transferring the solution to the NMR tube with a clean, dry pipet. Undissolved solids can severely reduce the quality of spectra, so solid samples should be filtered using a Pasteur filter pipet into a clean, dry NMR tube. The volume of solution in the tube should be 0.4–0.5 mL. Add additional pure solvent as necessary.

It is very easy to contaminate the solvent if a dirty Pasteur pipet is used to remove solvent from the supply. **Be sure to use a clean, dry pipet every time that solvent is removed from the solvent bottle.** It is very frustrating to try to determine the composition of an unknown if added impurity peaks must be accounted for as well.

How to Prepare a Sample for FT NMR

Sample preparation for and operation of high-field FT NMR spectrometers is significantly different than for CW instruments. Solutions to be analyzed by FT NMR should be approximately ten times less concentrated than for low-field work. Weigh out 5–10 mg of sample into a clean, tared vial. Add about 0.75 mL of a deuterated solvent, usually $CDCl_3$ containing TMS, and thoroughly mix to dissolve. Using a Pasteur pipet, transfer the dissolved sample to a Pasteur filter pipet that is placed in a clean, dry 5-mm NMR tube. Adjust the volume to the correct column length specified by the instructor by adding pure solvent as needed. Carefully cap the NMR tube and shake to thoroughly mix.

Structural Identification from the NMR Spectrum

The following six steps should be taken to determine the structure of an organic compound from its NMR spectrum.

1. **From the formula, if known, calculate the elements of unsaturation (unsaturation number or degrees of unsaturation).** A good first step is to find out if the organic molecule contains rings or multiple bonds. To do this, calculate the unsaturation number (U) from the molecular formula

$$U = \frac{(2C + 2) - H}{2}$$

where C is the number of carbon atoms and H is the number of hydrogen atoms in the molecule. If the molecule contains atoms other than carbon and hydrogen, the following rules apply in calculating the unsaturation number:

Halogens count the same as hydrogens.

Nitrogen atoms count as 1/2 carbon.

All other atoms, such as oxygen or sulfur, are not counted.

Three examples are shown below:

Molecular formula	Unsaturation number
$C_4H_6O_2$	2
$C_6H_4Cl_2$	4
CH_5N	0

The unsaturation number is equal to the total number of rings and/or multiple bonds in a compound. Once the unsaturation number is known, the number of double bonds, triple bonds, or rings can be determined. A ring or a double bond counts as one element of unsaturation, a triple bond counts as two elements of unsaturation, and a benzene ring counts as four elements of unsaturation.

Examples

Unsaturation number	Implication
0	No double bonds, triple bonds, or rings
1	One ring or one double bond
2	One triple bond or two rings or double bonds or some combination thereof
3	One triple bond and one double bond or ring or some combination thereof
4	Often a benzene ring (1 degree for the ring and 1 for each of the double bonds)

$U = 1$

$$\overset{O}{\underset{\|}{CH_3CCH_3}}$$

$U = 2$

$U = 3$

$U = 4$

2. **Examine the spectrum.** Determine the number of equivalent types of protons from the number of signals for the compound.
3. **Integrate the spectrum.** Determine the ratios of protons.
4. **Determine the types of protons present.** Examination of the number of signals and chemical shifts often reveals the general nature of the compound.

Chemical shift	Implication
$\delta 0.9–1.5$	Methyl, methylene, and methine protons
$\delta 2–2.5$	Protons adjacent to a carbonyl group, benzylic hydrogens, or allylic hydrogens.
$\delta 2.5$	Sharp singlet, (1H) - alkynyl proton
$\delta 3–4$	Protons on a carbon adjacent to an oxygen or halogen
$\delta 5–6$	Alkene protons: coupling constant of 0–2 Hz—geminal alkene; coupling constant of 5–12 Hz—*cis* alkene; coupling constant of 12–23 Hz—*trans* alkene; or proton on carbon attached to two oxygens or halogens
$\delta 7–8$	Aromatic ring protons
$\delta 9–10$	Aldehyde proton
$\delta 10–13$	Carboxylic acid proton

5. **Look for characteristic splitting patterns.** Splitting patterns and coupling constants further enhance the information obtained from the chemical shifts. Characteristic patterns are listed below:
   a. An ethyl group occurs as a triplet (which integrates to 3H) and a quartet (which integrates to 2H). The triplet is always further upfield.

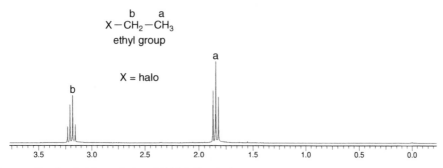

SOURCE: Reprinted with permission of Aldrich Chemical.

b. An isopropyl group occurs as a doublet (which integrates to 6H) and a multiplet (a heptet, actually, which integrates to 1H). Often, the outer peaks of multiplets can't be seen.

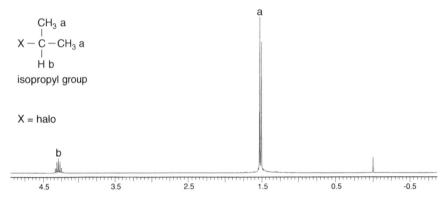

SOURCE: Reprinted with permission of Aldrich Chemical.

c. A *tert*-butyl group appears as a singlet (which integrates to 9H).

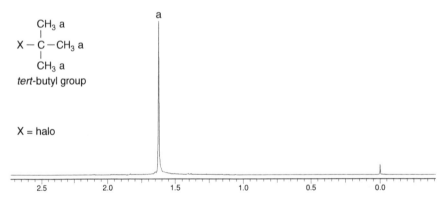

SOURCE: Reprinted with permission of Aldrich Chemical.

d. Barring overlapping signals, a singlet that integrates to 3H is usually one methyl group; a signal that integrates to 6H is usually two equivalent methyl groups; and a signal that integrates to 9H is usually three equivalent methyl groups.

6. **Put it all together.** Draw a structure that fits the elements of unsaturation, the chemical shifts, and splitting patterns. To practice these skills, try the following problem. Additional problems are given at the end of this exercise.

Example: A compound with the formula $C_5H_{10}O$ gives the ^1H NMR spectrum shown in Figure 2N-15. Determine the structure of the compound.

Solution

Unsaturation Number:	$U = \dfrac{(2C+2)-H}{2} = \dfrac{(2(5)+2)-10}{2} = 1$
Integration:	Signal a is 0.52; signal b is 0.26; signal c is 0.09. Dividing through by smallest number gives a ratio of approximately 6H for signal a, 3H for signal b, and 1H for signal c.
Spectral Analysis:	The presence of three signals indicates three types of hydrogens. One element of unsaturation means there is a ring or a

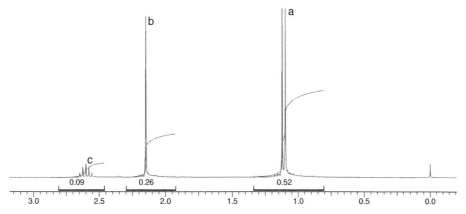

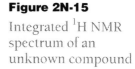

Figure 2N-15

Integrated ^{1}H NMR spectrum of an unknown compound

SOURCE: Reprinted with permission of Aldrich Chemical.

double bond. No signal at δ7–8 indicates the absence of aromatic protons. No signal at δ5–6 indicates the absence of alkenyl protons. A singlet around δ2.1 implies a methyl group attached to a carbonyl since there are no aromatic protons. The absence of signals for protons in the δ3.5–4 region rules out the possibility of a cyclic ether.

Splitting patterns: **Signal a:** a doublet of 6H implies two methyl groups attached to a carbon with one H; **Signal b:** a singlet of 3H implies one methyl group attached to a carbon with no H; **Signal c:** a heptet of 1H implies one hydrogen on a carbon that is adjacent to carbons with 6H (outer peaks of multiplets are often not seen). This splitting pattern is characteristic of an isopropyl group.

Structure: The compound must have a carbonyl group, since it is obviously not an alkene. Since there is no aldehydic proton signal around δ9–10, the compound could be a ketone. The methyl group at δ2.1 must be directly bonded to the carbonyl. The isopropyl group must be bonded on the other side of the carbonyl.

Identity: The compound is 3-methyl-2-butanone.

Practice problems for ^{1}H NMR spectroscopy are given in Exercise N.3.

3-methyl-2-butanone

Introduction to ^{13}C NMR Spectroscopy

In addition to hydrogen (^{1}H), other nuclei that possess an odd number of protons or neutrons (or both) have nuclear spins and are capable of showing resonance. In organic chemistry, the most important of these nuclei is ^{13}C. Like ^{1}H NMR spectroscopy, ^{13}C nuclear magnetic resonance spectroscopy (^{13}C NMR) can give detailed information about the different types of carbon in the compound.

Unfortunately, ^{13}C NMR spectroscopy is roughly 6000 times less sensitive than ^{1}H NMR spectroscopy because ^{13}C is much less abundant than ^{1}H (1.108% abundant versus 99.8%). This means that only about one of every 100 carbon atoms will have a nuclear spin. The remaining 99 atoms are ^{12}C, which do not have a nuclear spin.

Due partly to the low natural abundance of ^{13}C nuclei, ^{13}C NMR spectra must be obtained by Fourier Transform (FT) analysis of the free induction decay. In high-field NMR, the entire ^{13}C spectral width is irradiated briefly leading to excitation of each type of ^{13}C nucleus present. This process is repeated many times over a period of several minutes or hours. The resulting free induction decay is processed using computer-programmed FT methods to give ^{13}C NMR spectra. For further information, consult the references at the end of this Technique M.

The spectral width for ^{13}C nuclei is much larger than for ^{1}H nuclei (about $\delta 200$). Therefore, it is unusual to have different types of ^{13}C nuclei that have exactly the same chemical shift. Just like ^{1}H NMR, ^{13}C nuclei have characteristic chemical shift values. For example, carbon atoms of methyl groups have chemical shifts of $\delta 0$–35. Carbons bonded to electronegative atoms such as bromine, oxygen, and nitrogen appear downfield. Aromatic carbons have chemical shifts of approximately $\delta 110$–165 while alkenyl carbons have chemical shifts of approximately $\delta 100$–150. Typical values of ^{13}C chemical shifts are listed in Table 2N-3.

^{13}C Nuclei have a spin of $^{1}/_{2}$, meaning that there are two spin states, just as in ^{1}H NMR. ^{13}C NMR spectra are usually obtained using noise decoupling, a technique of simultaneous irradiation of all carbon and hydrogen nuclei. This technique simplifies ^{13}C spectra by removal of all C$-$H coupling. This, together with the unlikely positioning of ^{13}C nuclei next to one another, results in singlets for all carbon nuclei. Noise-decoupled ^{13}C spectra are not integrated, as peak areas do not correspond to the number of carbons in the signal.

The ^{13}C NMR spectrum for 2-vinylpyridine in $CDCl_3$ solvent is shown in Figure 2N-16. If you look closely, you can observe seven signals, corresponding to the seven nonequivalent carbons in 2-vinylpyridine. In general, there is one signal for every type

Table 2N-3 ^{13}C NMR Chemical Shifts

Type of carbon	Approximate δ value
Alkyl	$\delta 0$–50
C$-$Cl, C$-$Br	$\delta 20$–50
C$-$N; amines	$\delta 30$–60
C$-$O; alcohols, ethers	$\delta 50$–275
Alkynyl	$\delta 70$–90
Alkenyl	$\delta 100$–150
Aromatic	$\delta 110$–165
Nitrile	$\delta 115$–125
C=O; carboxylic acids, esters	$\delta 165$–180
C=O; ketones, aldehydes	$\delta 180$–220

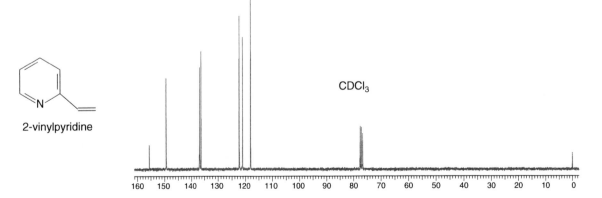

2-vinylpyridine

CDCl₃

Figure 2N-16 ^{13}C NMR spectrum of 2-vinylpyridine

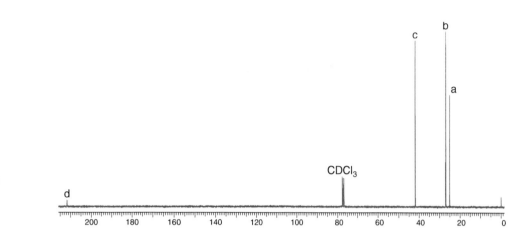

Figure 2N-17 ^{13}C NMR spectrum of cyclohexanone

SOURCE: Reprinted with permission of Aldrich Chemical.

of carbon present in the molecule. The three peaks at δ77.5 are due to the solvent, deuterochloroform.

Cyclohexanone has four different types of carbons and four signals in the ^{13}C NMR. The ^{13}C NMR spectra of cyclohexanone is shown in Figure 2N-17. The carbonyl carbon is far downfield, around δ215, and is very small. This signal may be easily missed. The triplet at δ77.5 is due to deuterochloroform.

Off-Resonance Decoupling

A second decoupling technique is sometimes used in ^{13}C NMR spectroscopy. This technique, called off-resonance decoupling, eliminates all coupling between carbons and hydrogens that are farther than one bond apart. This means that each carbon is coupled only to hydrogens that are directly attached to that carbon. Each signal will be a singlet, doublet, triplet, or quartet depending upon whether there are 0, 1, 2, or 3 hydrogens attached to the carbon atom. In the case of very simple organic compounds, this technique can be used to determine the number of hydrogens bonded to each carbon. Splitting patterns in off-resonance decoupled ^{13}C NMR spectra are listed here.

Structure	Number of hydrogens bonded	^{13}C NMR signal
—C—	0	singlet (s)
—C—H	1	doublet (d)
H—C—H	2	triplet (t)
H—C—H	3	quartet (q)

Solvents for ^{13}C NMR Spectroscopy

The most common solvent in NMR is $CDCl_3$. In the spectrum of 2-vinylpyridine, notice that the signal for $CDCl_3$ consists of three peaks of equal height, due to C–D coupling, at $\delta 77.5$. Deuterium has a spin of 1, resulting in three spin states. High-field instruments lock on the deuterium NMR signal. Other common deuterated solvents for ^{13}C NMR include C_6D_6 and CD_3COCD_3, which give signals at $\delta 128.0$ for deuterobenzene and at $\delta 29.8$ and $\delta 206.5$ for deuteroacetone. Table 2N-2 on page 139 lists properties of NMR solvents.

How to Prepare a Sample for ^{13}C NMR Spectroscopy

Weigh out 20–40 mg of sample into a clean, tared vial. Add about 0.75 mL of a deuterated solvent, usually $CDCl_3$, and mix to dissolve. Using a Pasteur pipet, transfer the dissolved sample to a Pasteur filter pipet that is placed in a clean, dry 5-mm NMR tube. Using a ruler, adjust the liquid column length to the height specified by the instructor by adding pure solvent. Carefully cap the NMR tube and shake to thoroughly mix.

General Approach to Determining an Unknown Structure

^{13}C NMR spectra are normally used in conjunction with IR and ^{1}H NMR spectra. Taken together, the structures of most simple organic compounds can be deduced. For some simple organic compounds, proton-decoupled or off-resonance decoupled ^{13}C NMR spectra may be sufficient to determine the structure of the compound. A general procedure of seven steps for structure determination follows.

1. **Determine the elements of unsaturation (unsaturation number or degrees of unsaturation) from the formula, if known.** This number will indicate the number of double bonds, triple bonds, and/or rings that are in the molecule.

$$U = \frac{(2C + 2) - H}{2}$$

2. **Examine the IR spectrum (if available).** The IR spectrum is helpful in determining which functional groups are present in the molecule.
3. **Examine the ^{1}H NMR spectrum (if available).** The integration, splitting patterns, and chemical shifts of the protons can provide important information about the general structure of the compound.
4. **Examine the proton-decoupled ^{13}C NMR spectrum.** Determine the number of magnetically unique carbon atoms from the number of signals in the spectrum. Remember that the height of the peak in the proton-decoupled ^{13}C NMR spectrum does not usually correlate with the number of carbons in the compound; however, a very small peak is frequently an indication of a quaternary carbon.
5. **Examine the off-resonance decoupled ^{13}C NMR spectrum (if available).** Determine the number hydrogens attached to each carbon atom. (Alternately, this information can be obtained from the ^{1}H NMR spectrum.)
6. **Use the ^{13}C Chemical Shift Table (Table 2N-3).** Correlate the chemical shift with the hybridization of the carbon and proximity to electronegative atoms.
7. **Assemble the fragments so that each atom has the correct number of bonds.**

An example will illustrate this approach.

Example: Figure 2N-18 shows the proton noise-decoupled spectrum of an unknown organic molecule with the molecular formula $C_{11}H_{15}NO$. The three signals at $\delta 77.5$ are due to the deuterochloroform. The multiplicities were obtained from the off-resonance

**Chemical Shifts
and Multiplicities:**
a. 13.2q
b. 47.3t
c. 112.1d
d. 128.1s
e. 133.4d
f. 152.6s
g. 191.2d

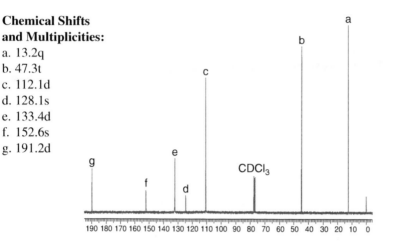

Figure 2N-18

^{13}C NMR spectrum of
an unknown
compound

Source: Reprinted with permission of Aldrich Chemical.

spectrum (s = singlet, d = doublet, t= triplet, q = quartet). The IR and ^{1}H NMR spectra of this compound are not available. From the noise-decoupled and off-resonance decoupled ^{13}C NMR alone, determine the structure of this compound.

Solution

First, calculate the elements of unsaturation. The unsaturation number is 5. There is a good possibility that the compound is aromatic.

Next, count the number of signals in the ^{13}C NMR spectrum. Frequently there may be signals in the spectrum due to the solvents, such as a singlet for TMS at $\delta 0$ and three peaks of equal height at $\delta 77.5$ for CDCl$_3$. This spectrum shows seven singlets, representing seven different types of carbon in the molecule. These peaks are labeled a–g. Notice that there are eleven carbons in the formula but only seven unique types of carbon.

Much information may be ascertained from the chemical shifts of the signals. Two of the peaks are upfield. Peaks "a" and "b" must be sp^3 hybridized. Peak "b" is further downfield, so the carbon must be bonded to an electronegative atom like nitrogen, oxygen, or a halogen. Since no halogen atom is present, this carbon must be directly bonded to the nitrogen or oxygen atom. There are four signals between $\delta 110$ and $\delta 150$, which is the aromatic region. Having four magnetically different carbon atoms would seem to indicate a *para-* disubstituted aromatic ring. Peak "g" is far downfield, indicative of a carbonyl (C=O) group. Therefore the carbon represented by peak "b" must be attached to a nitrogen atom. It might be possible to infer the structure of the molecule from this spectrum alone.

Now consider the data from the off-resonance decoupled spectrum. Since peak "a" is split into a quartet, there must be three hydrogens bonded to the carbon. This is a methyl group (CH$_3$–). Peak "b" is split into a triplet; hence it is a CH$_2$– group. Peaks "c" and "e" are aromatic and both have one hydrogen attached; peaks "d" and "f" are singlets with no hydrogens attached. This must be the point of attachment of the substituents. Peak "g" is a doublet, indicating that one hydrogen is bonded to the carbonyl. This must then be an aldehyde functionality. The fragments are shown here.

Fragments "a" and "b" obviously combine to form an ethyl group. The formula shows two more carbon atoms. It is apparent that there are actually two ethyl groups in the compound (in order to satisfy the valency of the nitrogen atom). The identity of the organic compound is 4-(N,N-diethylamino)benzaldehyde. (For further information on assigning carbons labeled "c," "d," "e," and "f," consult one of the references at the end of Technique N.)

Exercise N.1: Recording a ^{1}H NMR Spectrum

Prepare a sample for ^{1}H NMR, as directed by the instructor. Record and analyze the spectrum. Prepare a detailed report, interpreting the spectrum.

Exercise N.2: Recording a ^{13}C NMR Spectrum

Prepare a sample for ^{13}C NMR, as directed by the instructor. Record and analyze the spectrum. Prepare a detailed report, interpreting the spectrum.

Exercise N.3: ^{1}H NMR Spectral Problems

From the spectral information and molecular formula, propose structures that are consistent with the data for 3-A through 3-G. The spectra are 300 MHz FT-NMR ^{1}H NMR spectra. The NMR solvent is CDCl$_3$ containing TMS.

Problem 3-A
C$_4$H$_9$Cl
δ0.9 (3H)
δ1.5 (2H)
δ1.7 (2H)
δ3.5 (2H)

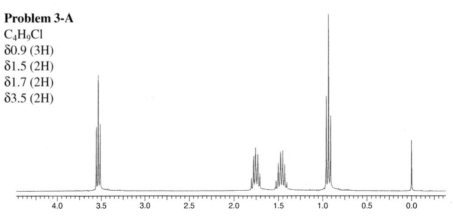

SOURCE: Reprinted with permission of Aldrich Chemical.

Problem 3-B
C_4H_9Cl
δ1.0 (6H)
δ1.9 (1H)
δ3.4 (2H)

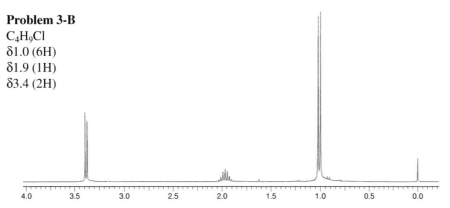

SOURCE: Reprinted with permission of Aldrich Chemical.

Problem 3-C
C_7H_{16}
δ0.9 (12H)
δ1.0 (2H)
δ1.6 (2H)

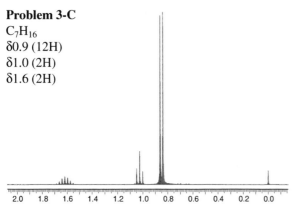

SOURCE: Reprinted with permission of Aldrich Chemical.

Problem 3-D
$C_5H_{10}O$
δ1.1 (6H)
δ2.5 (4H)

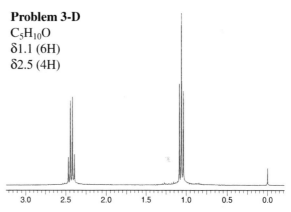

SOURCE: Reprinted with permission of Aldrich Chemical.

Problem 3-E
C_8H_8O
δ2.5 (3H)
δ7.2−7.7 (4H)
δ10.0 (1H)

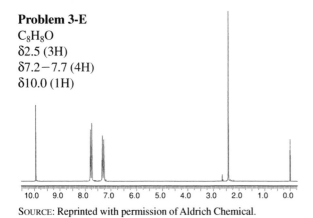

SOURCE: Reprinted with permission of Aldrich Chemical.

Problem 3-F
$C_6H_{14}O$
δ0.9 (6H)
δ1.6 (4H)
δ3.4 (4H)

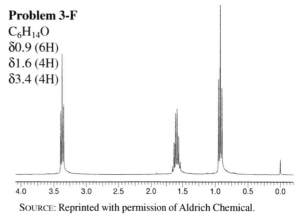

SOURCE: Reprinted with permission of Aldrich Chemical.

Problem 3-G.   From the data given below, determine the structure of each of the following unknown compounds:

1. C_3H_7Br: δ1.71 doublet (6H); δ4.29 heptet (1H)
2. C_4H_9Cl: δ1.62 singlet
3. C_4H_8O: δ1.1 triplet (3H); δ2.1 singlet (3H); δ2.5 quartet (2H)
4. $C_4H_{10}O_2$: δ3.4 singlet (6H); δ3.6 singlet (4H)
5. $C_8H_{10}O$: δ1.5 triplet (3H); δ4.1 quartet (2H); δ7.0–7.8 multiplet (5H)

Exercise N.4: ^{13}C NMR Spectral Problems

Predict the structure of the organic compounds that give each of the spectra labeled 4-A through 4-C. Note that the three signals at δ77.5 are due to solvent, deuterochloroform.

Problem 4-A

$C_6H_{14}O$

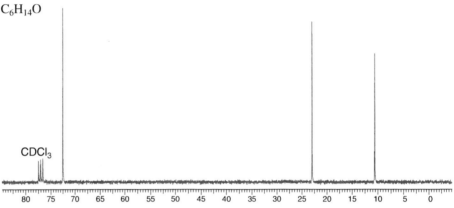

SOURCE: Reprinted with permission of Aldrich Chemical.

Problem 4-B

$C_7H_{12}O$

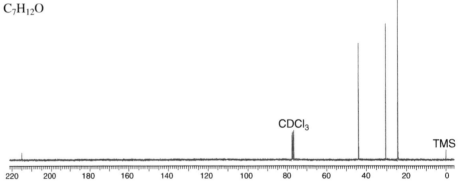

SOURCE: Reprinted with permission of Aldrich Chemical.

Problem 4-C

C_8H_{10}

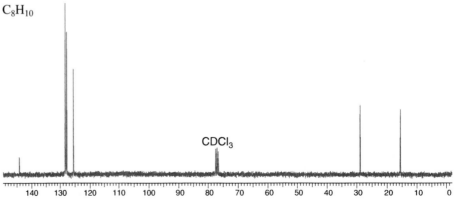

SOURCE: Reprinted with permission of Aldrich Chemical.

Exercise N.5: Spectral Identification Using ^{1}H and ^{13}C NMR

Predict the structure of the organic compounds that give the ^{1}H and ^{13}C NMR spectra labeled 5-A through 5-C.

Problem 5-A

$C_{11}H_{14}O_2$

$\delta 1.0$ (3H)

$\delta 1.5$ (2H)

$\delta 1.7$ (2H)

$\delta 4.4$ (2H)

$\delta 7.4 - 8.1$ (5H)

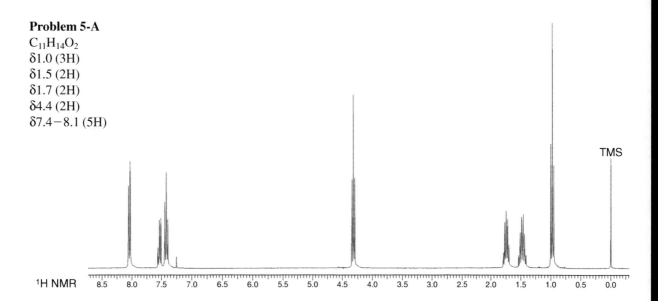

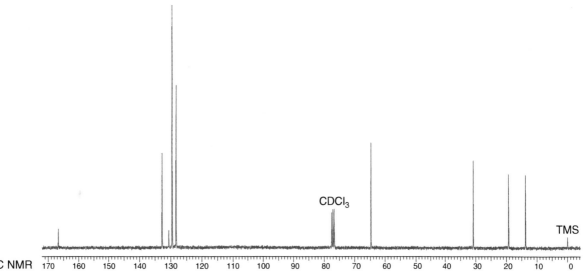

SOURCE: Reprinted with permission of Aldrich Chemical.

Problem 5-B
C_7H_8O
$\delta 3.7$ (3H)
$\delta 7 - 7.3$ (5H)

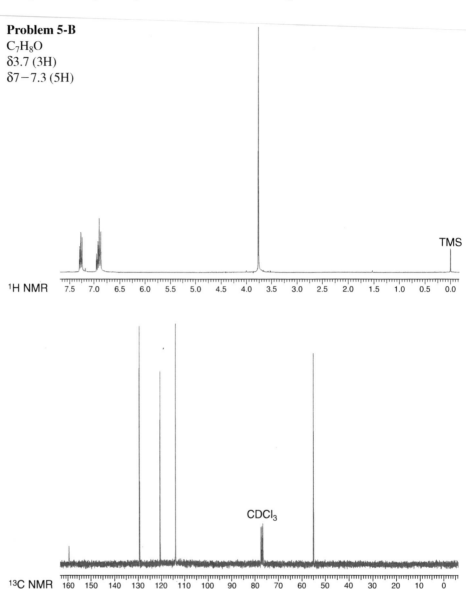

SOURCE: Reprinted with permission of Aldrich Chemical.

Questions

1. Are the effects on chemical shifts of attached electronegative atoms additive? Explain.

2. Explain how to differentiate between acetic acid and methanol using ^{1}H NMR spectroscopy.

3. Explain why protons on alcohols show singlets in the CW ^{1}H NMR spectra.

4. How could ^{1}H NMR spectroscopy be used to differentiate between 2-butanone and methyl propanoate?

Problem 5-C
C_4H_6O
δ2.2 (3H)
δ5.9−6.3 (3H)

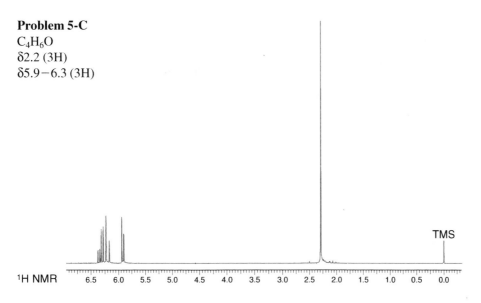

¹H NMR

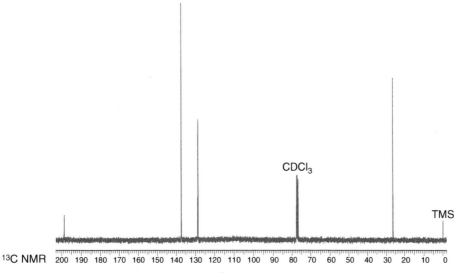

¹³C NMR

SOURCE: Reprinted with permission of Aldrich Chemical.

5. The ¹H NMR spectrum of cyclohexane shows one singlet. If the sample is cooled to −80°C, the spectrum changes. Predict the spectrum of the cooled cyclohexane and explain why the spectrum changes as the solution is cooled.

6. What is the purpose of TMS?

7. Predict the chemical shift of the protons in methyllithium (CH_3Li).

8. A specific proton in an organic compound has a chemical shift of δ3.4 in a 60 MHz NMR spectrum. What will be the chemical shift if the spectrum is recorded using a 90 MHz NMR instrument?

9. The coupling between two protons in an alkene is 10.8 Hz at 60 MHz. What will be the value of the coupling constant between these same two protons at 200 MHz?

References

Abraham, R. J., Fisher, J., and Loftus, P. *Introduction to NMR Spectroscopy.* New York: Wiley, 1992.

Breitmaier, E. *Structure Elucidation by NMR in Organic Chemistry.* Chichester, England: Wiley, 2002.

Kemp, W. *Organic Spectroscopy.* 3d ed. New York: W. H. Freeman and Company, 1991.

Lambert, J. B., Shurvell, H. F., Lightner, D., and Cooks, R. G. *Organic Structural Spectroscopy.* Upper Saddle River, NJ: Prentice-Hall, Inc., 1998.

Pavia, D., Lampman, G., and Kriz, G. *Introduction to Spectroscopy: A Guide for Students of Organic Chemistry.* 3rd ed. Pacific Grove: Brooks/Cole, 2001.

Silverstein, R. M., and Webster, F. X. *Spectrometric Identification of Organic Compounds.* 6th ed. New York: Wiley, 1998.

Technique O: Ultraviolet and Visible Spectroscopy

Introduction

IR and NMR spectroscopy both play an extremely important role in structure identification in the organic laboratory. Ultraviolet and visible (UV-vis) spectroscopy plays a supporting role. The wavelength ranges for UV and visible spectroscopy are shown in Figure 2O-1.

Conjugated unsaturated compounds, such as dienes, trienes, and aromatic compounds, absorb UV light. Extensively conjugated molecules, such as methyl orange, β-carotene, and β-chlorophyll, are colored and absorb visible light. Most saturated organic molecules, such as hexane and ethanol, do not absorb UV (>200 nm) or visible light. Alkenes absorb UV light, but the wavelength of maximum absorption (λ_{max}) falls below the normal UV region (< 200 nm). Carbonyl compounds, such as aldehydes and ketones, also absorb weakly in the UV region.

UV spectra can be useful in the analysis of conjugated molecules and visible spectra can be useful in the analysis of colored compounds. Spectra may be used qualitatively to determine absorption maxima and minima or quantitatively to measure concentrations of substances. UV spectroscopy is generally of more use in organic chemistry than visible spectroscopy because many more organic compounds absorb UV light than absorb visible light. An advantage of UV-vis spectroscopy is that very small amounts of sample are required—much smaller than the amounts needed for IR and NMR spectroscopy.

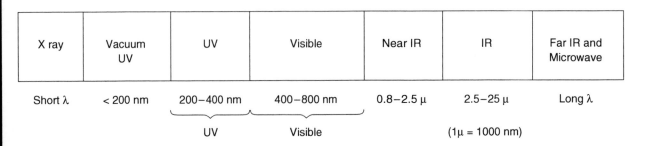

X ray	Vacuum UV	UV	Visible	Near IR	IR	Far IR and Microwave
Short λ	< 200 nm	200–400 nm	400–800 nm	0.8–2.5 μ	2.5–25 μ	Long λ
		UV	Visible		(1μ = 1000 nm)	

Figure 2O-1   Relationship of UV and visible light to other forms of electromagnetic radiation

Theory

Certain compounds absorb UV and visible radiation because an outer π or nonbonding electron is excited from its ground state to an excited state. For conjugated dienes, trienes, and aromatics, an electron from the highest lying π molecular orbital is excited to a π^* molecular orbital. This effect is illustrated in Figure 2O-2 using molecular orbital theory for the π molecular orbitals of 1,3-butadiene. The theory is also used for comparison with the π molecular orbitals of a simple alkene, ethene.

The highest occupied and lowest unoccupied orbitals are labeled HOMO and LUMO, respectively. The energy difference between the HOMO and LUMO is greater for ethene than for 1,3-butadiene. Therefore the energy required for excitation is greater for ethene (164 kcal/mole at 171 nm) than for 1,3-butadiene (129 kcal/mole at 217 nm). The greater the number of conjugated double bonds, the closer the energies of the LUMO and the HOMO. More extensively conjugated substances are colored and have HOMO and LUMO energies that are very close. This requires less energetic, longer wavelength light for excitation. The wavelengths required for excitation fall in the visible region for colored organic compounds such as Methyl orange dyes, β-carotene, and β-chlorophyll.

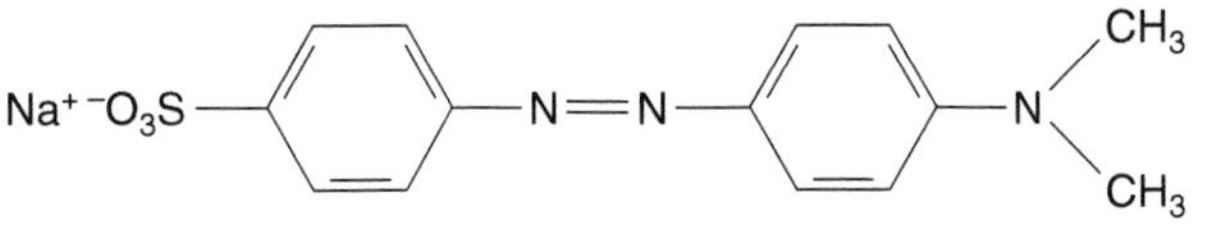

Methyl orange

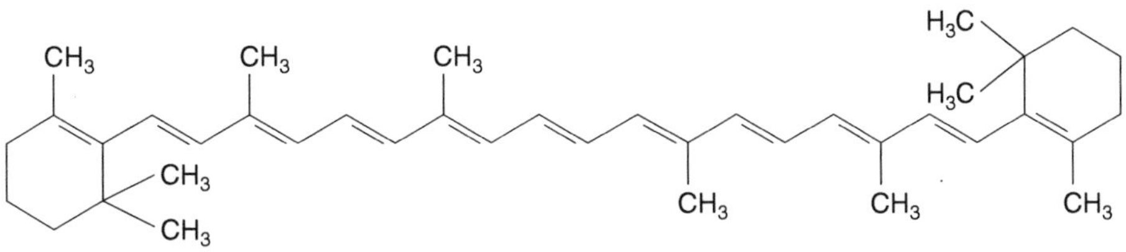

β-Carotene

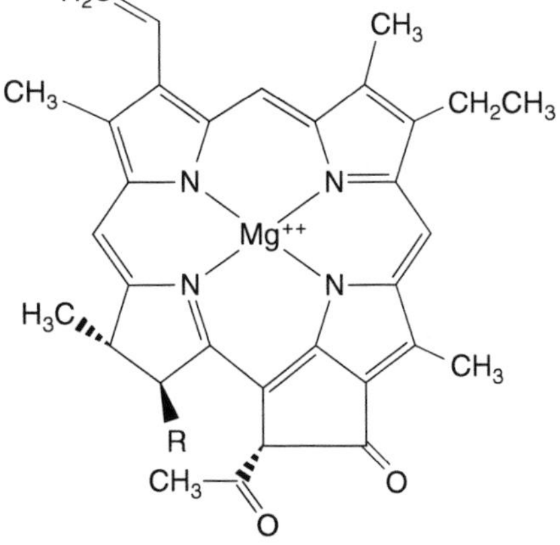

$R = \text{phytylpropanoyl} = C_{24}H_{43}O_2$

β-Chlorophyll

UV spectra are plots of absorbance or molar absorptivity versus wavelength (200–360 nm). Compounds having extended conjugation have λ_{max} values at longer

Figure 20-2

Molecular orbital diagrams for ethene and 1,3-butadiene

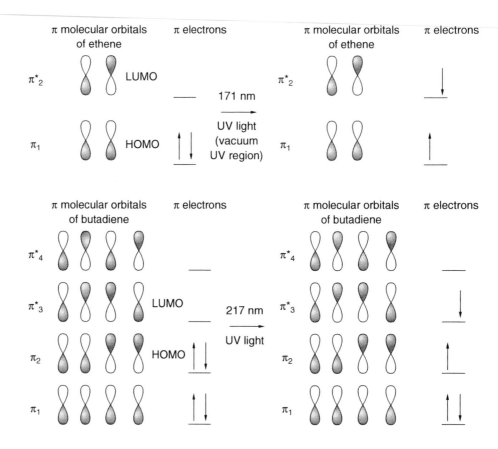

wavelengths than less conjugated compounds. Aromatic compounds, such as benzonitrile and toluene, absorb in the UV region due to their conjugated structures. UV spectra consist of very broad peaks and valleys because the electronic states responsible for UV absorption have many vibrational and rotational states. Electronic excitation may start and end at any of several different energy levels, resulting in a wavelength range of excitation. Examples of typical UV spectra are shown in Figure 20-3.

Uses of UV-Visible Spectroscopy

Qualitative Analysis

UV spectroscopy can be used to distinguish between conjugated and nonconjugated unsaturated compounds. Some examples of λ_{max} values for unsaturated hydrocarbons are given below.

Compound	λ_{max} (nm)	Number of conjugated double bonds
1-pentene	177	0
1,4-pentadiene	178	0
1,3-butadiene	217	2
1,3-pentadiene	224	2
trans-1,3,5-hexatriene	253, 263, 274	3
benzene	256	3
toluene	261	3

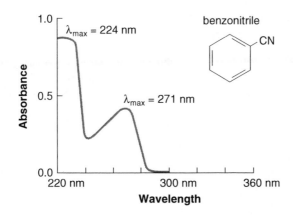

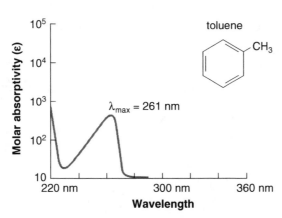

Figure 20-3

Examples of UV spectra

Substitution patterns of conjugated dienes and trienes can be predicted using the Woodward-Fieser rules (Wade 2003, pp. 1211–1215). Alkylated, conjugated dienes and aromatic compounds have λ_{max} values at longer wavelengths than 1,3-butadiene.

Quantitative Analysis

Beer's Law states that the intensity of absorption is proportional to the concentration of a dilute solution of an absorbing compound, where A = absorbance, c = concentration (M), d = width of the sample cell (usually 1 cm), and ε= molar absorptivity (L/mole-cm):

$$A = \varepsilon cd$$ **Beer's Law**

Molar absorptivity (ε) is a measure of how effectively a compound absorbs radiation at a particular wavelength. Molar absorptivity values at specific wavelengths are physical constants that are available in spectral catalogs (Weast 1973). The magnitude of ε values depends upon the type of excitation. Transitions that are inefficient, such as the n → π* transition of carbonyl groups, have low ε values. (An n → π* transition is excitation of a nonbonding electron to an antibonding π* orbital.) The π → π* transition of the π bond of alkenes is very efficient. These transitions have large ε values.

Applications of Beer's Law

Example 1: A sample of 1,3-cyclohexadiene has a molar absorptivity of 10,000 at the λ_{max} of 259 nm. The measured absorbance reading is 0.35 and the width of the sample tube is 1.0 cm. The concentration of the sample can be determined from the equation $A = \varepsilon cd$. For this sample, c is calculated to be 3.5×10^{-5} M.

Example 2: UV spectroscopy can be used to monitor reaction rates. Because absorbance is proportional to concentration, UV and visible spectroscopy can be used to monitor changes of absorbing species during a reaction. A plot of 1/absorbance versus time for the second-order reduction of an azo dye at 520 nm is given below. The plot of 1/A versus time should give a straight line for a second-order reaction as shown in Figure 2O-4.

In Example 2, the concentration of azo dye decreases with time as the dye is reduced. The intensity of absorption decreases at the λ_{max} of the azo dye linearly as a function of 1/A. In this way UV and visible spectroscopy can be used as a convenient tool for kinetics studies.

How to Operate a Spectronic 20

1. Turn the instrument power on and allow the instrument to warm up for several minutes.
2. Set the dial to the desired wavelength for analysis. Use the left knob to set % transmittance to zero.
3. Prepare a cuvette or test tube containing a blank. The blank is usually a solution containing everything but the absorbing species. Place the container in the sample compartment and adjust the % transmittance to 100% using the right knob.
4. Remove the tube containing the blank and replace it with a test tube containing the solution to be analyzed. If the same container is used for the blank and the sample, rinse out the container several times with the sample solution.
5. Record the % transmittance and calculate absorbance.

$A = 2 - \log\%T$

A	1/A	Time (minutes)
.83	1.20	0
.81	1.23	1
.80	1.25	2
.76	1.31	4
.73	1.37	6
.70	1.42	8
.65	1.53	12
.58	1.71	16
.54	1.82	20

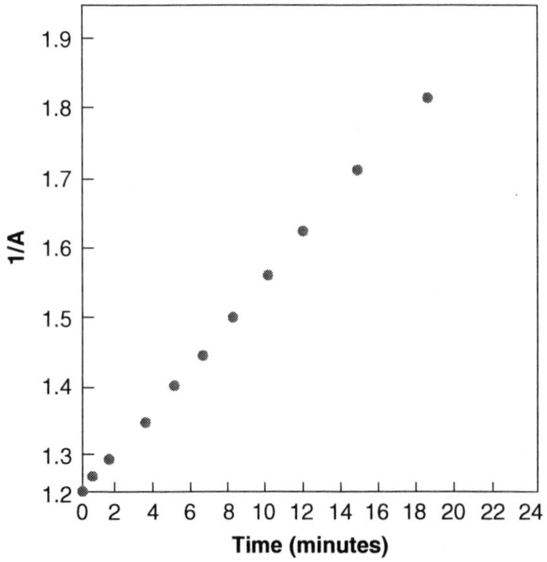

Figure 2O-4   Second-order rate plot for data from kinetics experiment monitored using a Spectronic 20

6. Repeat steps 3–5 as necessary for the same sample and for diluted samples.
7. Turn off the instrument power unless the instrument is to be used again soon.

How to Operate a UV-Visible Spectrometer

1. Turn the instrument power on. If necessary, set the instrument for either UV or visible use. In the UV, a deuterium lamp is used and should be turned on. A tungsten lamp is used for analyses in the visible region.
2. Using a matched pair of fused silica cuvettes, fill each cuvette with solvent being used for the experiment.
3. Zero the baseline and scan the wavelength region of interest. In the UV, the region to be scanned is generally from 200 to 400 nm. Use 400–800 nm for a scan in the visible region. There should be little or no absorption observed throughout the scan. A trace of the baseline should be flat.
4. Remove the cuvette from the sample compartment, but leave the cuvette containing solvent in the reference compartment. Empty the sample cuvette and add some of the solution to be analyzed and rinse. Repeat this twice and then fill the cuvette with the solution to be analyzed. Return the cuvette to the sample compartment.
5. Scan the region of interest and be sure that the desired absorbance readings are achieved. If the absorbance reading is lower than 0.30, try increasing the concentration of the solution being analyzed and repeat the scan. If the solution is too concentrated, the absorbance reading will be too high and the sample solution should be diluted. For quantitative work, the absorbance reading at the λ_{max} should be between 0.3 and 0.8 absorbance units.
6. Obtain a recording of the spectrum. Be sure to label the spectrum with name, date, sample identification, solvent, and concentration of the sample, if known.
7. Remove all solutions from the cuvettes. Be careful, as the matched cells are expensive. Return the cuvettes to their storage container and turn off the instrument power.

Questions

1. The energy of UV light is 70 kcal/mole at 400 nm and 140 kcal/mole at 200 nm. Why is UV radiation damaging to the eyes and skin? (Hint: Think about the energy required to break a C−C bond.)
2. Which is more energetic: 235 nm or 325 nm light? Explain.
3. Why is UV spectroscopy used more frequently in organic chemistry than visible spectroscopy?
4. Using the structure of methyl orange as an example, draw resonance forms to show how conjugation extends throughout the molecule.
5. Depict the π molecular orbitals for 1,3,5-hexatriene. Show the electron occupancy of each orbital. Label the LUMO and HOMO. Is the expected wavelength for UV excitation at a longer or shorter wavelength than that for 1,3-butadiene?
6. Calculate the molar absorptivity (ε) of benzene at 260 nm for a solution of benzene in ethanol where the concentration of benzene is 3.3×10^{-3} M and the absorbance reading is 0.70 using a 1-cm cell.
7. Is toluene a good solvent for UV spectroscopy? Explain.

References

Pavia, D., Lampman, G., and Kriz, G. S. *Introduction to Spectroscopy.* 3rd ed. Pacific Grove: Brooks/Cole, 2001.

Wade, L. G. Jr. *Organic Chemistry.* 5th ed. Upper Saddle River, NJ: Prentice-Hall, 2003.

Weast, R. C., ed. *Atlas of Spectral Data and Physical Constants for Organic Compounds.* Boca Raton, FL: CRC Press, 1973.

Technique P: Mass Spectrometry

Principles of Mass Spectrometry

In mass spectrometry (MS), an organic molecule is bombarded with an electron beam in an evacuated chamber. This causes the molecule to lose an electron, forming a molecular ion $M^{+\bullet}$ (a radical cation). The energy required is usually sufficient to cause the molecular ion to fragment into carbocations and radicals. When carbocations are formed, an equal number of free radicals are also formed, but these are not normally detected. Only the positively charged species are usually detected in MS. The ionization and fragmentation processes take place in the gas phase in a very highly evacuated environment (10^{-5} torr). This process, called electron impact (EI), is shown here for methane.

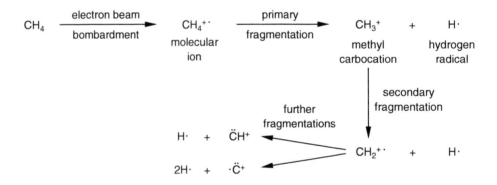

The $CH_4^{+\bullet}$ radical cation is called the molecular ion. Generally, only the molecular ions and cations from primary fragmentation are important in MS. (There are some exceptions.) In MS, the methyl carbocation is formed by primary fragmentation of $CH_4^{+\bullet}$. For methane, a plot of the mass to charge ratio (m/z) versus relative abundance of fragments shows that the molecular ion at m/z 16 and the primary fragment at m/z 15 are the most abundant ions. Because the molecular masses of CH_4 and $CH_4^{+\bullet}$ differ only by the mass of one electron, the position on the m/z scale for CH_4^+ gives the molecular mass of the compound. Since methane (CH_4) is neutral, it is not detected in mass spectrometry. Fragments resulting from secondary and higher-order fragmentations are not very abundant and are generally not observed as major fragments in MS. However, the mass spectrum of a very simple molecule, such as CH_4, demonstrates the principle of successive fragmentations. The mass spectrum of methane is shown below as a bar graph. The largest peak is called the base peak. In this case, the base peak and the molecular ion peak are the same.

methane, CH_4
$CH_4^{+\cdot}$
CH_3^+
$\cdot CH_2^+$
$\cdot\ddot{C}^+$
$\ddot{C}H^+$
Relative intensity
or percent of base peak
100
80
60
40
20
0
10 11 12 13 14 15 16 17 18 19 20
m/z

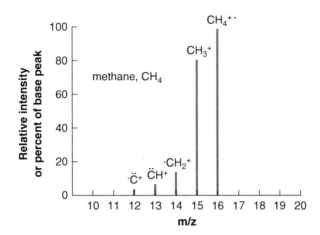

Simple alkanes show a peak corresponding to the molecular ion, $M^{+\bullet}$. For ethane, this peak occurs at m/z 30. For propane, the molecular ion peak is m/z 44. The molecular ion of propane can lose a hydrogen atom to form an isopropyl carbocation of m/z 43. The primary propyl carbocation is also possible, but less likely, because it is less stable than the secondary carbocation. The predominant fragmentation affords an ethyl carbocation of m/z 29 (base peak) and a methyl radical. Formation of the alkyl radical via carbon-carbon cleavage is preferable to formation of a hydrogen atom (radical).

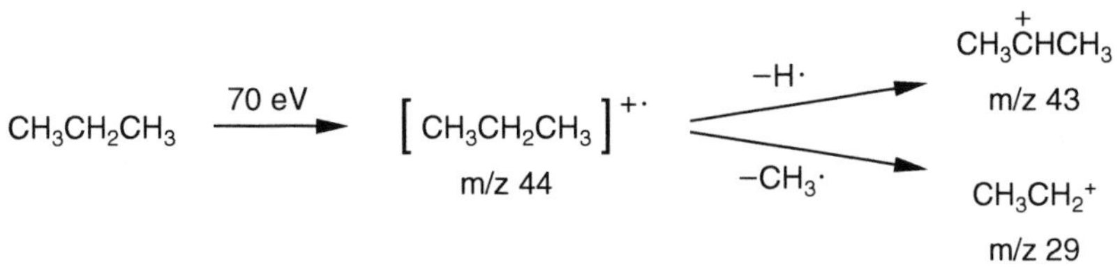

$CH_3CH_2CH_3$
70 eV
$[CH_3CH_2CH_3]^{+\cdot}$
m/z 44
$-H\cdot$
$-CH_3\cdot$
$CH_3\overset{+}{C}HCH_3$
m/z 43
$CH_3CH_2^+$
m/z 29

The mass spectrum of butane shows the $M^{+\bullet}$ at m/z 58 and fragment peaks at m/z 43 and 29, corresponding to the isopropyl carbocation (after rearrangement from the initially formed propyl carbocation) and ethyl carbocation. For isobutane, loss of methyl radical furnishes the isopropyl carbocation directly at m/z 43 and this is the expected fragmentation. Loss of hydrogen radical to give a *tert*-butyl carbocation is unlikely due to the easier bond breaking of a C−C (85 k cal/mol) versus a C−H (95 k cal/mol) bond.

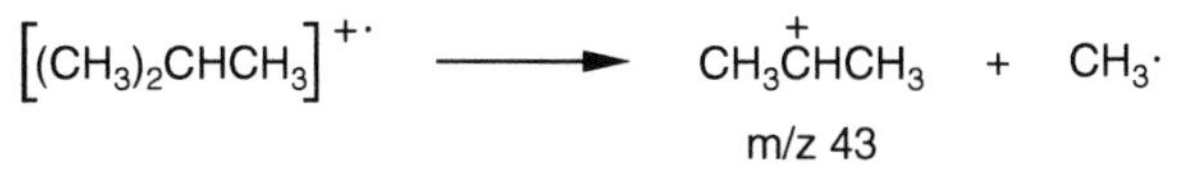

$[(CH_3)_2CHCH_3]^{+\cdot}$
$CH_3\overset{+}{C}HCH_3$
+
$CH_3\cdot$
m/z 43

Mass spectra of higher-molecular-weight alkanes also show abundant C_3 and C_4 fragments. Spectra of more complex molecules show clusters of bars, indicating masses of the more stable fragments. For example, an isopropyl cation at m/z 43 can lose a hydrogen atom to form a propenyl cation at m/z 42 and the propenyl cation can lose a hydrogen radical to form an allyl cation at m/z 41. In MS, just as in solution, the more stable fragments are those that are the more stable carbocations. However, because of the high energies involved, numerous carbocations can be formed in MS that are not typically formed in solution. Also, losses of hydrogen atoms and other neutral species can occur for carbocation fragments in MS while this is not observed for carbocations in solution.

In addition to breaking apart to give a fragment and a free radical, molecular ions may also lose a stable neutral molecule, such as ethylene. Loss of a neutral molecule from the molecular ion results in a new radical ion, which for compounds containing carbon and hydrogen or carbon, hydrogen, and oxygen, has an even-numbered mass. Loss of ethylene is observed for cyclic alkanes such as cyclohexane. The mass spectrum of cyclohexane is shown below. Peaks are observed for positive fragments, but not for radicals or neutral molecules.

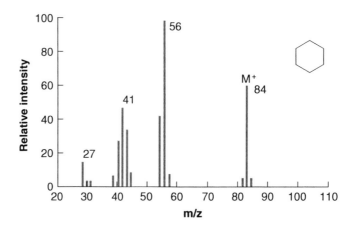

Note that the molecular weight of cyclohexane is an even number (84). Molecular masses of molecules without nitrogen or that have an even number of nitrogens are even numbered. In the example above, cyclohexane has a mass of 84. The molecular ion peak, $M^{+\bullet}$, has the identical mass of 84. Odd-numbered fragments (41 and 27) are carbocations. However, the even-numbered peak at m/z 56 is not a carbocation. It is a radical cation that has a mass that is 28 mass units less than the mass of cyclohexane due to loss of ethylene. The largest peak (base peak) is observed at m/z 56. This peak cannot be a carbocation because the mass of the fragment is even and carbocations such as CH_3^+, $C_2H_5^+$, etc., have odd-numbered masses. The fragment at m/z 56 must result by loss of a neutral molecule (ethylene) from the molecular ion.

$$\left[\bigcirc \right]^{+\bullet} \longrightarrow \left[\, \right]^{+\bullet} + \quad CH_2{=}CH_2$$

m/z 84   m/z 56 ·
                                       $C_4H_8^+$

The fragment at m/z 41 is due to an alkenyl carbocation. There is no simple cleavage pattern to get from the radical cation m/z 56 ion to the m/z 27 fragment. The latter fragment is a result of secondary fragmentation. These fragmentations are depicted here.

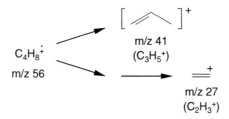

Fragmentation Patterns

It is important to understand where peaks occur (at which m/z values) and why some peaks are large and others are small. The base peak is the largest peak and corresponds to a stable, positively charged fragment or molecule. Odd-numbered fragments of compounds that contain no nitrogen or an even number of nitrogens will show large peaks if they correspond to stable carbocations. The abundance varies for each compound and depends on the mass of the compound, the skeletal structure (straight chain or branched), and the types of functional groups that are present. Some of the more important fragmentation pathways for representative functional classes of compounds are presented in this section.

The principal objective is to become familiar with basic patterns of fragmentation so that the main fragments in a mass spectrum will be identifiable. Cleavage generally favors formation of the most stable cations and radicals, although the radicals are not seen in MS. Primary carbocations have very little stability, and tertiary carbocations are usually the most stable fragments. Stabilization of the radical (formed in producing the carbocation) is also important. Fragmentation also depends upon the relative bond strengths of bonds being broken. Breaking a C—H bond requires more energy than breaking a C—C bond. Allylic and benzylic C—H bonds are broken more easily than other C—H bonds. (Refer to the table of bond dissociation energies in Table 2P-1.)

Alkanes

Of the common cleavage patterns, simple cleavage is observed for alkanes. In simple cleavage, a carbon-carbon bond is broken from the molecular ion. Some carbon-carbon bonds are more likely to break than others. For 3-methyloctane, cleavage is more likely to occur near the branching carbon because the resulting carbocations are secondary rather than primary. In this case there are two possibilities, because cleavage may occur on either side of the branching carbon (C—3). (A third possibility for breaking a tertiary C—H bond is less likely.) The base peak in the MS of 3-methyloctane is at m/z 99. Other peaks occur at m/z 57 and m/z 113.

Table 2P-1   Bond Dissociation Energies[*]

Bond	kJ/mol	kcal/mol
CH_3-H	435	104
CH_3CH_2-H	410	98
$(CH_3)_2CH-H$	397	95
$(CH_3)_3C-H$	380	91
C_6H_5-H	460	110
$CH_2=CH-H$	452	108
$CH_2=CH-CH_2-H$	372	89
$C_6H_5CH_2-H$	356	85

[*]Bond dissociation energies refer to the single bond indicated in structural formula for each compound.

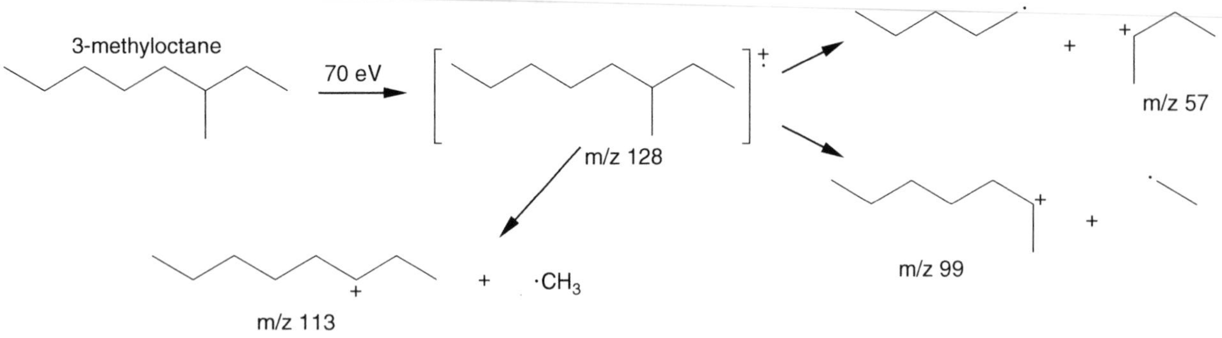

3-methyloctane

$$\xrightarrow{70\ eV}$$

m/z 128

m/z 113   +   ·CH₃ (·CH$_3$)

m/z 99

m/z 57

The odd electron can also remain with the secondary carbon, giving m/z 71 and 29 peaks. Although observable in the MS of 3-methyloctane, these peaks are much smaller.

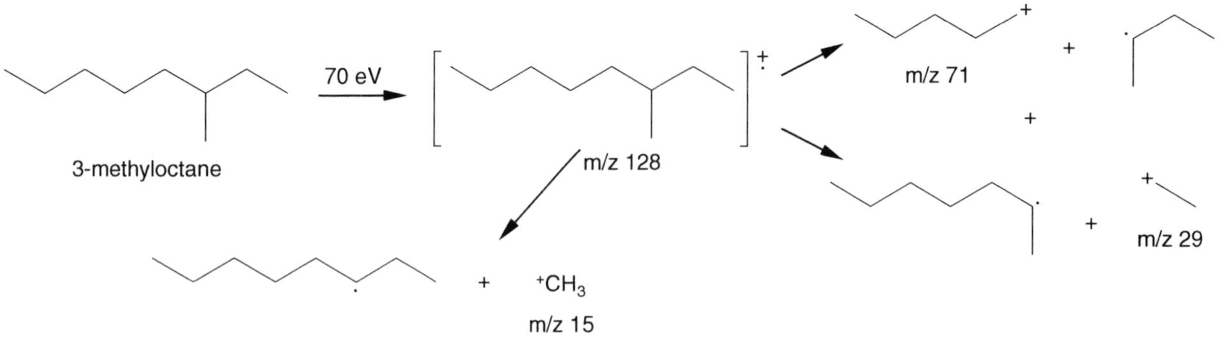

3-methyloctane

$$\xrightarrow{70\ eV}$$

m/z 128

+ $^+CH_3$

m/z 15

m/z 71

m/z 29

Alkenes

Alkenes often fragment to yield allylic ions. For example, the base peak in the mass spectrum of 1-heptene is m/z 41 due to formation of the allyl cation.

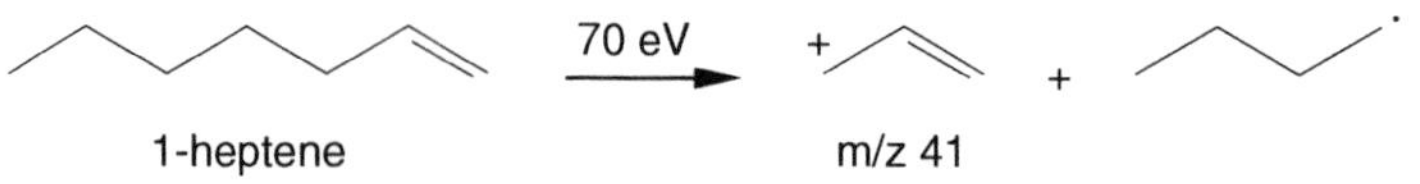

1-heptene $\xrightarrow{70\ eV}$ m/z 41

Cyclic alkanes and alkenes often split out stable neutral molecules such as ethylene or substituted ethylenes. The resulting cationic fragment is the radical cation of an alkene or a diene. For example, cyclohexene is known to give ethylene as shown below. This is similar to a retro Diels-Alder reaction.

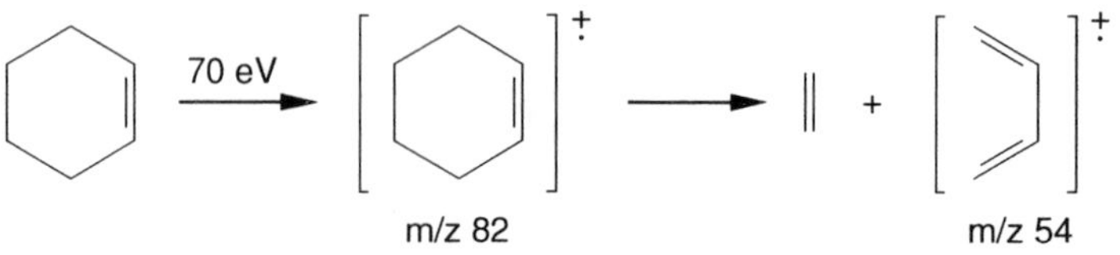

$$\xrightarrow{70\ eV}$$

m/z 82 $\longrightarrow$ ‖   +

m/z 54

Aromatic Compounds

Aromatic compounds that contain alkyl side chains often cleave to yield benzylic carbocations as the main fragmentation path. The benzylic ions initially formed rearrange to the more stable tropylium ions.

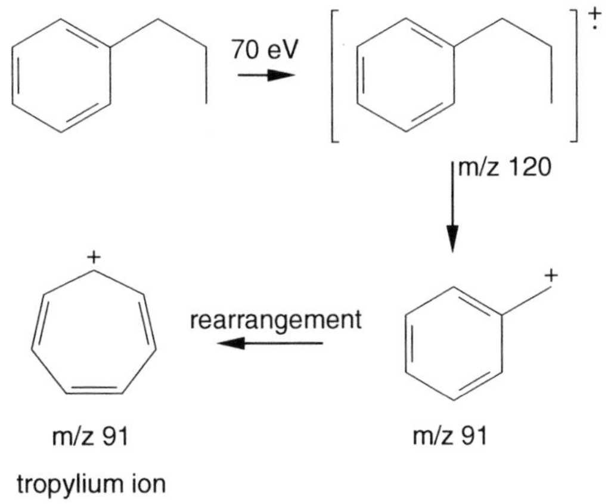

m/z 91
tropylium ion

m/z 91

Compounds with Heteroatoms

Molecules containing oxygen, nitrogen, halogens, or other heteroatoms may undergo a similar type of cleavage, called α-cleavage, where the driving force is formation of resonance-stabilized cations. An example is 4-heptanone, where α-cleavage yields a four-carbon acylium ion and a propyl radical.

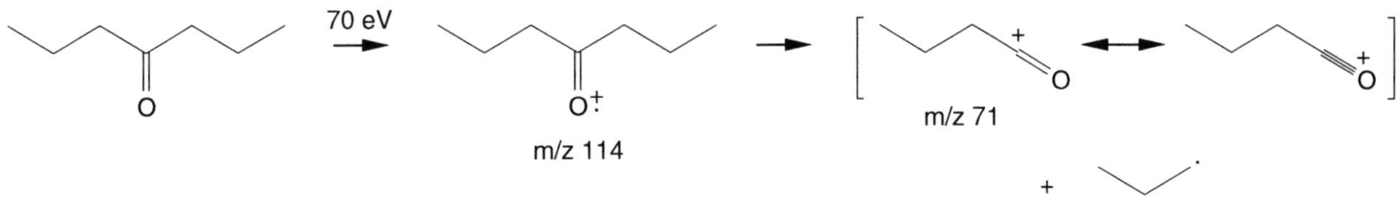

Another example of a simple α-cleavage involving an ether is shown below.

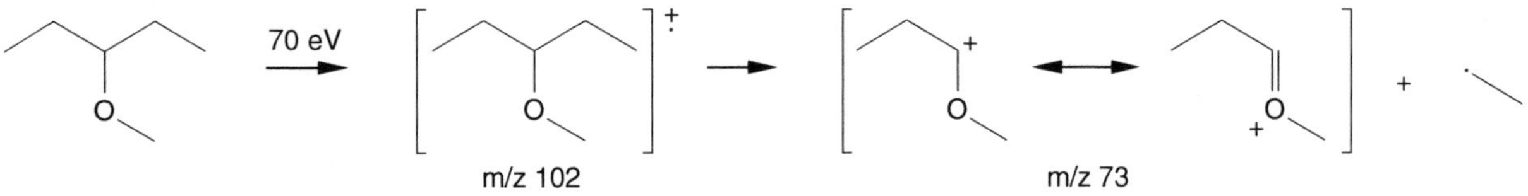

Compounds with More Than One Heteroatom

Cleavage will generally occur at a more substituted carbon bearing the heteroatom as shown. This is what would be predicted based on the relative stabilities of the carbocations formed.

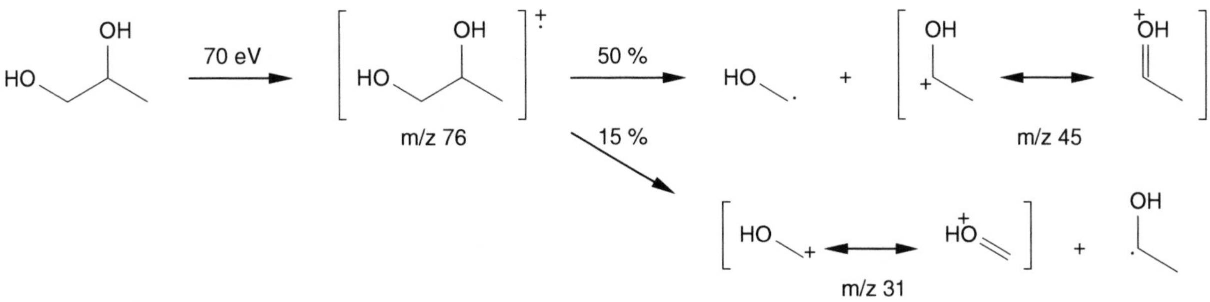

Among different heteroatoms, less electronegative atoms exert a greater stabilizing effect than more electronegative atoms. This effect may be seen from the example below. Note that cleavage is favored to give the ion that contains the nitrogen atom. This is what would be predicted based on the electronegativities of the atoms.

Carbonyl Compounds

Carbonyl compounds, such as aldehydes, ketones, and esters, may also split off neutral molecules from the molecular ion. In this case, not only is a neutral molecule expelled, but there is also a transfer of an atom via rearrangement. The rearrangement is called a McLafferty rearrangement. In order to give the rearrangement there must be at least a three-carbon chain attached to the carbonyl and the γ-carbon must have at least one hydrogen. It is the γ-hydrogen that is transferred during rearrangement. The resulting radical cation, which has an even mass number, can also give further fragmentation.

The ester below lacks enough carbons to give a McLafferty rearrangement, but it has a large side chain that gives rise to a related rearrangement.

Molecular Ion Peak

A principal use of MS is to determine molecular mass. This is effective for most compounds provided that a particular compound gives a molecular ion peak. In high resolution MS (HRMS), the mass of the molecular ion peak is measured precisely to four decimal places. This value may be compared with tables of masses (Silverstein and Webster 1998). For example, both $C_2H_3N_2$ and C_3H_5N have masses of 55, but the exact mass of $C_2H_3N_2$ is 55.0297 and that of C_3H_5N is 55.0422. This difference is easily determined in HRMS. Not all compounds give large molecular ion peaks; some branched alkanes and alcohols do not show a molecular ion peak at all. Generally, more highly branched compounds are likely to fragment more easily and show smaller molecular ion peaks. On the other hand, cyclic compounds, aromatics, normal chain compounds, and alkenes generally show large molecular ion peaks. Occasionally, the molecular ion will also be the base peak (largest peak in the spectrum), but more often a stable fragment will be the base peak.

Isotopes

MS is particularly valuable for compounds that contain chlorine and bromine atoms. Substances that contain chlorine or bromine atoms give large molecular ion peaks and

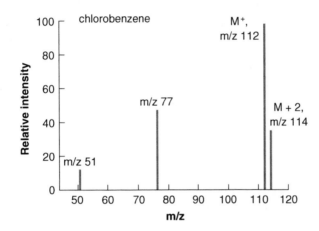

very sizable peaks (called M + 2 peaks) two mass units higher than the molecular ion peaks. For example, chlorobenzene shows a molecular ion peak at m/z 112 and an M + 2 peak at m/z 114. This latter peak is given by molecules (25% of the total) that contain ^{37}Cl rather than ^{35}Cl. The relative abundance of this peak is about one-third of the molecular ion abundance, since the relative abundances of ^{35}Cl and ^{37}Cl are roughly 75:25.

The MS of a monobrominated compound is similarly distinctive. The bromine isotopes of 79 and 81 are of equal abundance. Therefore, a compound containing one bromine atom will show M and M + 2 peaks that are of equal size. For example, bromobenzene shows two peaks of equal size (equal abundance) at m/z 156 and 158.

Compounds with more than one bromine or chlorine give additional isotope peaks (M + 4, M + 6, etc.). The m/z values and the abundance of these isotope peaks indicate the type and number of chlorine and bromine atoms present. Fluorine and iodine atoms have only single isotopes in natural abundance.

Gas Chromatography/Mass Spectrometry (GC/MS)

Gas chromatography/mass spectrometry (GC/MS) is a very important and useful instrumental method of analysis for organic substances. Applying this technique, a multicomponent mixture of volatile organic compounds is injected into a GC column through the injection port. This procedure is the same as for ordinary GC analysis (see Technique J). As the individual compounds are eluted, they are analyzed by a mass selective detector. Mass spectra are computed in less than a second and these may be analyzed during or after the GC run is completed. There are many applications. For example, the organic extract of a sample of water from a stream or a sample of drinking water may be analyzed for the presence of pesticides and herbicides.

Strategy for Solving Structural Problems Using MS, IR, and NMR

In practice, structural identification is usually done using NMR and IR. The IR spectrum is used to determine the types of functional groups that are present. Interpretation of the NMR spectrum gives specific structural information about the nature of the carbon skeleton and the types of attached protons. Sometimes it is necessary to get additional information and this is where MS may be useful. It is also conceivable that in certain situations, IR and NMR data may not be available, either because the compound in question is a constituent of a complex mixture or because there was not enough sample to obtain a good IR or NMR spectrum. One very favorable feature of MS is that only very small samples are needed for analysis. MS is also very useful for determining the molecular mass of the compound (although some compounds, such as alcohols and highly branched compounds, may not show a molecular ion peak) and for determining whether the compound contains bromine or chlorine. MS can also be helpful for identifying whether the compound contains an odd number of nitrogen atoms. To use MS for structural determination, follow the guidelines below.

Mass Spectrometric Analysis Guidelines

1. Consult your instructor for directions on how to prepare solutions for MS and GC/MS analyses.
2. Determine the molecular mass if possible. Remember that some alcohols and compounds that are highly branched may show very small or nonexistent molecular ion peaks.
3. Determine whether the compound contains bromine or chlorine or contains an odd number of nitrogens.
4. Map the major fragmentations observed by subtracting the masses of each fragment from the molecular mass. Refer to Tables 2P-2 for masses of fragment ions, 2P-3 for masses of fragment radicals, and 2P-4 for masses of neutral molecules expelled from molecular ions. Stabilized fragment ions, such as tertiary carbocations, allylic ions, acylium ions, and tropylium ions are seen most frequently as major fragment ions.
5. Propose fragmentation patterns to explain the presence of each fragment and the relative abundance of each fragment. It is usually possible to propose a likely structure or structures for an unknown.

Worked Examples of Spectral Analysis

MS of Unknown A (*Refer to spectrum on p. 169.*)

1. *Molecular weight:* The molecular ion is at m/z 182. An almost equally abundant peak is at m/z 184 (M + 2 peak).
2. *Analysis of nitrogen or halogens:* Presence of one bromine atom in the molecule is inferred because there are two peaks of approximately equal intensity in the area of the molecular ion. One peak is at m/z 184 and the other peak is at m/z 182. Two peaks are observed because bromine has two almost equally abundant isomers, ^{79}Br and ^{81}Br. The molecular ion is taken to be the peak with the lower mass, which contains ^{79}Br. The molecular mass is even, an indication that no nitrogen atoms or an even number of nitrogen atoms are present.

	Table 2P-2 Typical Mass Spectrometric Fragment Ions		**Table 2P-3** Typical Mass Spectrometric Radicals		**Table 2P-4** Typical Mass Spectrometric Neutral Molecules Formed

m/z	Cation
27	$C_2H_3^+$
29	$C_2H_5^+$
30	$CH_2NH_2^+$
31	CH_2OH^+, CH_3O^+
35	Cl^+
39	$C_3H_3^+$
41	$C_3H_5^+$
43	$C_3H_7^+$, $CH_3C{=}O^+$
53	$C_4H_5^+$
55	$C_4H_7^+$
57	$C_4H_9^+$
59	$CH_3OC{=}O^+$
65	$C_5H_5^+$
67	$C_5H_7^+$
69	$C_5H_9^+$
71	$C_5H_{11}^+$, $C_3H_7C{=}O^+$
75	$CH_3CH_2OC{=}O^+$
77	$C_6H_5^+$
79	Br^+
85	$C_6H_{13}^+$, $C_4H_9C{=}O^+$
91	$C_6H_5CH_2^+$, $C_7H_7^+$
99	$C_7H_{15}^+$
105	$C_6H_5C{=}O^+$
107	$C_6H_5CH_2O^+$, $HOC_6H_4CH_2^+$
127	I^+

Mass	Radical
15	CH_3
17	OH
27	$CH_2{=}CH$
29	CH_3CH_2
30	$CH_2{=}NH_2$
31	CH_3O, CH_2OH
35	Cl
41	$CH_2{=}CHCH_2$
43	C_3H_7, $CH_3C{=}O$
45	CH_3CH_2O
49	CH_2Cl
57	C_4H_9
59	$CH_3OC{=}O$
69	C_5H_9

Mass	Molecule
18	H_2O
26	$H{-}C{\equiv}C{-}H$
27	HCN
28	$CH_2{=}CH_2$
32	CH_3OH
36	HCl
42	$CH_2{=}C{=}O$, $CH_3CH{=}CH_2$
54	$CH_2{=}CHCH{=}CH_2$
78	C_6H_6
80	HBr
128	HI

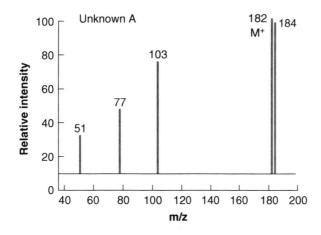

3. *Determination of fragment ions:* A large fragment ion at m/z 103 is indicative of loss of a bromine radical (having mass of either 79 or 81) giving a phenylethenyl cation. Also prominent are peaks at m/z 77, corresponding to the phenyl cation, and m/z 51, corresponding to secondary fragmentation of the phenyl cation. The phenyl cation loses the neutral molecule, acetylene (MW = 26), to form a cation containing four carbons and having m/z 51. These fragmentations are illustrated here.

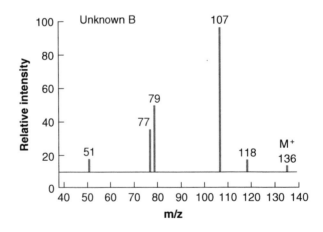

4. From the data available, unknown A appears to be either (Z) or (E)-1-bromo-2-phenylethene (β-bromostyrene). The distinction between Z and E isomers can be made by measuring coupling constants for the alkene protons in the ^{1}H NMR spectra.

(E)-1-bromo-2-phenylethene   (Z)-1-bromo-2-phenylethene

MS of Unknown B

1. *Molecular weight:* The molecular ion peak indicates a molecular weight of 136.
2. *Analysis of nitrogen or halogens:* The molecular mass is even, an indication that no nitrogen atoms or an even number of nitrogens are present.
3. *Determination of fragment ions:* Alcohols frequently show very small or nonexistent molecular ion peaks. This is because the molecular ion easily loses water to give an M-18 fragment. In this case that fragment appears at m/z 118. The ion at m/z 107 is due to loss of an ethyl radical (mass = 29) from the molecular ion. The 107 peak is the base peak in this spectrum and it is due to a benzylic ion that is stabilized by an adjacent −OH group. The fragment at m/z 77 is due to a phenyl cation, formed from the molecular ion. The peak at m/z 51 is a result of secondary fragmentation of the phenyl cation, resulting in the loss of acetylene. The peak at m/z 79 is also a

result of secondary fragmentation and it may result from loss of CO from the 107 peak. It is usually not possible to assign identities to all fragments or to ascribe all fragmentation pathways with certainty. These fragmentations are summarized here.

4. The likely structure of Unknown B is 1-phenyl-1-propanol.

1-phenyl-1-propanol

MS of Unknown C

1. *Molecular weight:* The molecular weight is 59.
2. *Analysis for nitrogen or halogens:* The odd-numbered molecular ion peak indicates the presence of a nitrogen atom.
3. *Determination of fragment ions:* Loss of a 29 radical indicates cleavage to form an ethyl radical and a resonance stabilized iminium ion fragment ion ($CH_2=NH_2^+$) of m/z 30.
4. Unknown C is 1-aminopropane ($CH_3CH_2CH_2NH_2$).

Exercise P.1: Solving Problems in Mass Spectrometry

In this exercise, you will learn to apply the basic principles of mass spectrometry, the important modes of fragmentation of organic compounds, and the methods of interpretation of mass spectra of simple organic compounds.

1. For each of the spectra labeled a–f below, determine the molecular mass. Explain how it is possible to tell if nitrogen, chlorine, or bromine is present.
2. For each of the spectra labeled a–f, identify the major features and suggest identities of major fragments. It will not generally be possible to do this for all fragment

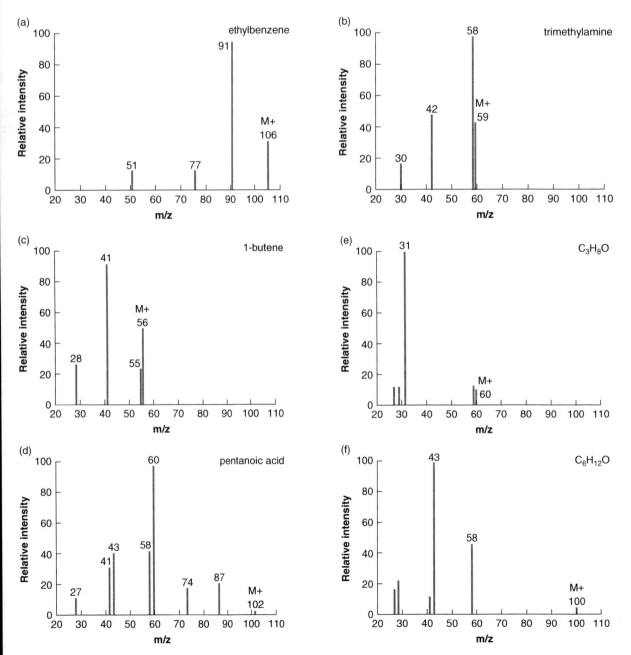

peaks. For spectra where only molecular formulas are furnished, calculate the elements of unsaturation (see Technique N) before proceeding with the MS analysis.

Questions

1. What ion fragments are expected from the mass spectrum of ethane?
2. Is 2-methylpropane expected to show a large ion fragment at m/z 29? Explain.
3. What is special about the stability of an ion fragment of m/z 41?
4. For 3-methyloctane, which end of the molecule is more likely to undergo fragmentation? Explain.
5. What major ion fragment is expected from the mass spectrum of acetone? Explain using structural drawings.
6. Illustrate the cleavage pattern for:
    a. ethylene glycol.
    b. ethylenediamine.
7. What major ion fragment is expected from the mass spectrum of ethylbenzene?
8. Predict the mass spectrum of 2-chloropropane. Explain.
9. Illustrate the McLafferty rearrangement for:
    a. 2-hexanone.
    b. propyl acetate.
10. *Library project:* Locate a journal article by either J. B. Fenn or K. Tanaka. Write a brief summary highlighting the significance of the work. Fenn and Tanaka received the 2002 Nobel Prize in chemistry along with K. Wuthrich.

References

Lambert, J. B., Shurvell, H. F., Lightner, D., and Cooks, R. G. *Organic Structural Spectroscopy*. Upper Saddle River, NJ: Prentice-Hall, Inc., 1998.

Pavia, D., Lampman, G., and Kriz, G. *Introduction to Spectroscopy: A Guide for Students of Organic Chemistry*. 3rd ed. Pacific Grove: Brooks/Cole, 2001.

Silverstein, R. M., and Webster, F. X. *Spectrometric Identification of Organic Compounds*. 6th ed. New York: Wiley, 1998.

Technique Q: Molecular Modeling

Introduction

Chemists have sought ways to make perception of organic molecules more visual and ways to make the presentation of chemistry more exact and scientific. Theoretical chemists have successfully made each of these objectives possible by developing molecular modeling software. Most desktop computers are now fast enough to be able to handle the mathematical calculations required for molecular modeling.

Molecular modeling encompasses both the two-dimensional projection of molecules and the three-dimensional assembly of molecules and their manipulation. For computer modeling, projections can be presented in various ways including ball-and-stick, tube, bond-line, space-filling, and other projections. Molecular modeling of projected molecules enables the interpretation and use of estimates of physical data, such as energies, dipole moments, and electron densities based on force-field or quantum mechanical calculations. In this technique, we will discuss aspects of each of these features of molecular modeling and present exercises in calculating minimized energies of alternative conformations of simple organic molecules, predicting the relative stability of organic isomers, and calculating a number of physical properties.

Most students of organic chemistry have ready access to a molecular model kit. The next section on molecular modeling is a brief discussion of molecular model kits and their importance in learning organic chemistry. Use of these kits is encouraged in lecture and laboratory work.

Organic Molecular Models

Use of molecular model kits provides an excellent vehicle to help students visualize molecules and the spatial relationships between bonded and nonbonded atoms within molecules. Particularly important is the ability to see complex molecules in three dimensions, to physically rotate the models around single bonds, and to appreciate the very limited rotation of bonds within rings or multiple bonds. A common application is to visualize different conformations of rings, such as substituted cyclohexanes.

An important use of molecular models is assisting in the understanding of stereochemical relationships. Elements of symmetry can often be seen more easily than from two-dimensional drawings. Building models can also help the student understand relationships between structures. Model kits can be used to determine if structures are either superimposable or whether they are enantiomers or diastereomers.

Drawing Organic Molecules Using Computer Software

It is often necessary to be able to draw an organic structure prior to doing modeling studies. The structure may be represented as a bond-line drawing, a framework model showing bonds but not atoms, or a ball-and-stick model. Organic molecules can be drawn using commercial software. Several drawing programs are available for use on desktop computers. Among those that are primarily designed for drawing organic molecules are ACD/ChemSketch (Advanced Chemistry Development), ChemDraw (CambridgeSoft Corp.), ISIS/Draw (MDL Information Systems Inc.), and ChemWindow (Bio-Rad Laboratories). Structural drawings can be readily pasted or inserted into word processing and presentation documents. These documents are useful in preparing laboratory reports.

Molecules may be also represented as space-filling drawings or as electrostatic potential map drawings. By representing molecules in these ways, a clearer picture emerges of the electron clouds within molecules. Calculations based upon models such as these fall within the realm of molecular modeling.

Molecular Modeling Using Computer Software

Until the recent era of fast personal computers, molecular modeling on the computer was confined to research laboratories equipped with expensive computers, with results reported in research articles in scientific journals. Calculations are now possible by anyone who owns a desktop computer equipped with molecular modeling software. Some molecular modeling programs employed in modeling studies, calculating energies, and estimating various physical properties are CAChe (CAChe Scientific, Inc.), CHARMM

(M. Karplus, Harvard), Chem3D (CambridgeSoft), Discover (Molecular Simulations, Inc.), MacroModel (Schrodinger), HyperChem (Hypercube, Inc.), Spartan (Wavefunction, Inc.), and SYBYL (Tripos, Inc.).

These programs and others like them facilitate learning in organic chemistry and learning in the organic laboratory. When we can model on a molecular basis what is happening in a reaction flask, it helps us to conceptualize and visualize physical processes such as distillation and chemical processes such as organic reactions and the mechanisms of these processes.

Two separate approaches are used in molecular modeling. One uses a subatomic approach that is based upon quantum mechanics and quantum mechanical approximations. The other treats atoms in a molecule as if they were connected by springs to certain other atoms in the molecule. This approach is faster and is known as molecular mechanics. In some cases, both approaches are used for different aspects of the calculations.

Sample calculations and exercises are included for the two types of modeling that follow. Students are encouraged to work through the sample calculations using computer software of their own and then to try the exercises at the end of each section. Additional exercises are included as critical thinking questions at the end of a number of the experiments. Molecular mechanics is discussed in the next section.

Molecular Mechanics

The potential energy of a molecule can be represented by the total contributions of energies of all molecular components. These contributions include bonding and nonbonding interactions.

$$PE = E = \Sigma E \text{ bonding interactions} + \Sigma E \text{ nonbonding interactions}$$

The bonding contributions are stretching energies of bonds summed over all bonds, bending and scissoring energies summed over all bonds, and torsional energies summed over all bonds. The nonbonding interactions summed over all bonds are electrostatic field effects through space and van der Waals forces between atoms that are nonbonded. The nonbonding forces may be attractive or repulsive.

$$E = \Sigma E \text{ stretching} + \Sigma E \text{ bending} + \Sigma E \text{ torsional} + \Sigma E \text{ field} + \Sigma E \text{ van der Waals}$$

Calculations of the force field begins with an estimate of the "look" of the molecule. This is usually a drawing of a molecule that you would make using one of the structural drawing programs. Each of the terms in the equation is then calculated using one of the modeling programs. The programs may include different levels of sophistication. For example, simple force-field calculations are done by considering the bonds as simple harmonic oscillators. More advanced force fields may take into consideration potentials beyond simple harmonic and may consider effects due to electronegativity differences of atoms and other effects. The more advanced force fields may require more calculation time, but they can give better agreement between calculated and experimental results. Among many applicable force fields are those known as MM2, MM3, and MM4; SYBYL and MMFF.

There are a few issues to keep in mind concerning calculated energies. The calculated energies can only be used as comparisons with one another. They are not absolute energies. The energy comparisons are roughly equivalent to enthalpy comparisons of molecules in the gas phase. Molecular mechanics can be used as an aid in evaluating relative energies of different conformations in conformational analysis. Entropy contributions are ignored in these calculations.

Sample Calculation 1: Bond Angles

Bond angles can be estimated using force-field calculations. To use 3-bromopropene as an example, if the initial drawing of the structure is drawn in one of the calculation software programs, the bond angles appear as 109° around the sp^3 carbon (C3) and as 102° around the sp^2 carbons (C1 and C2). Calculate the bond angles in the lowest energy conformation.

Solution: Use molecular mechanics to measure the minimum energy geometry. The H−C1−C2 bond angle is calculated to be 123.2° and the C2−C3−Br bond angle is calculated to be 114.8° for 3-bromopropene.

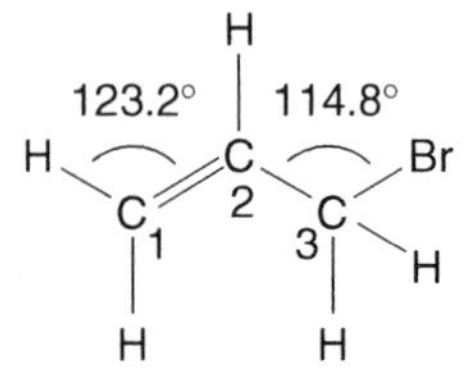

Sample Calculation 2: Dihedral Angles

Molecular mechanics calculations can furnish data on preferred dihedral angles and relative energies of conformations of molecules. Calculate the dihedral angle of the preferred conformation of 3-bromopropene. Calculate the relative energies of the preferred conformation and the conformation having a dihedral angle of 0°.

Solution: The dihedral angle for C1−C2−C3−Br of the energy-minimized (preferred conformation) of 3-bromopropene using a molecular mechanics MMFF calculation is 118.34°. The energies of different conformations of the molecule such as eclipsed or other conformations may also be calculated by constraining the C1−C2−C3−Br dihedral angle. The relative energy of the conformation having a dihedral angle of 0° is 3.56 kcal/mol higher than that of the preferred conformation. Conformations of 3-bromopropene and the designated dihedral angles are shown below.

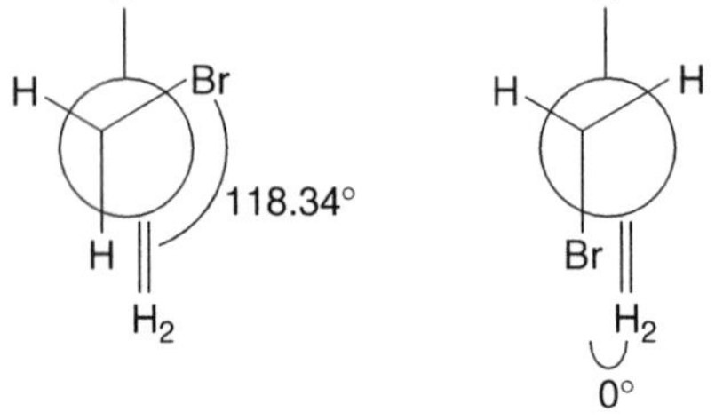

Sample Calculation 3: Conformational Energies

Relative energies of different conformations of molecules can be calculated, tabulated, and plotted. Determine the relative energies for ten different conformations of 1,2-difluoroethane? (The number of conformations selected can be set in the software program.

Solution: A tabulation of calculated conformational energies of 1,2-difluoroethane from 180° (anti conformation) to 0° (fluoro-fluoro eclipsed conformation) is shown on the next page.

1,2-Difluoroethane conformation; Dihedral angle	Relative energy (kcal/mol)
180° (anti)	0.00
160°	0.70
140°	2.16
120° (fluoro-hydrogen eclipsing)	2.86
100°	2.00
80°	0.89
60°	1.48
40°	4.23
20°	7.57
0° (fluoro-fluoro eclipsing)	9.06

Sample Calculation 4: Gauche, Anti, and Eclipsed Forms

Calculate the relative energies of the gauche and anti conformations of butane. How much more stable is the anti conformation than the eclipsed conformation having two eclipsed methyl groups? Compare your calculations with the experimental values given in your lecture text.

Solution: After drawing in the structure of butane, the program allows you to constrain the C2−C3 bond angle to 180° for the anti conformer. The calculated energy using SYBYL is 0.989 kcal/mol. Similarly, the energies for the 60° (gauche) and 0° (methyl-methyl eclipsed) conformers are 1.606 kcal/mol and 6.884 kcal/mol respectively. Now setting the anti conformation to 0 kcal/mol and recalculating gives a gauche energy of 0.617 kcal/mol and methyl-methyl eclipsed energy of 5.895 kcal/mol. These values compare favorably with the experimental values.

Relative Energies of Butane Conformers

Conformation	Calculated energy (kcal/mol)	Experimental energy (kcal/mol)
Eclipsed	5.895	Varies from 4 to 6 kcal/mol
Gauche	0.617	About 0.8
Anti	0	0

A different application of molecular mechanics concerns the interactions of molecules in a mixture. If organic molecules are mixed with water molecules, molecular mechanics predicts that the water molecules will attract one another and be at close proximity. This can be illustrated by drawing in two water molecules and three ethane molecules on the same screen (using one of the software programs). Energy optimization brings the water molecules together.

It is interesting to see how molecular mechanics calculations compare with experimental data. Being able to estimate the properties of molecules through calculation helps us to validate our theories of how atoms are connected in molecules and how molecules look and behave on a microscopic level.

Exercises Q1–3 are introductory examples that a student may encounter during the first part of an organic chemistry course. Additional assignments are included in several experiments in this text, including Experiment 5.1, 6.1, 8.2, 9.1 and subsequent experiments.

Exercises involving molecular mechanics calculations for the determination of molecular properties such as equilibrium geometries, strain energies, vibrational frequencies, and those involving calculations of energies of different conformers, their bond distances, and angles, may be found as questions in the Critical Thinking sections of several experiments in this text, including Experiments 3.7, 7.2 and later experiments.

Quantum Mechanics

The main advantage of molecular mechanics calculations is their relative speed and the ability to perform calculations on molecules having a thousand or more atoms. In the second approach for calculating molecular properties, quantum mechanical modeling is considered. This approach requires more calculation time and is limited to smaller molecules, usually those having one thousand or fewer atoms. However, this limitation is not severe for many practicing experimentalists.

Modeling using quantum mechanical approximations depicts a molecule as consisting of electron clouds containing embedded pointlike positively charged nuclei. Although they may require more time than molecular mechanics calculations, quantum mechanics calculations are generally used to model various possible transition states and to predict their relative stabilities. Quantum mechanics calculations can be used to predict product distributions for reactions that may give multiple products.

Hartree-Fock calculations are based upon the Schrodinger wave equation, but assume motionless nuclei (Born-Oppenheimer approximation) and use an approximation known as the linear combination of atomic orbitals (LCAO). Although the assumptions and resulting approximations are considerable, it is still possible to derive useful qualitative and quantitative information from the calculations. Hartree-Fock models are used in calculations of transition-state energies for molecules having fewer than one hundred atoms. Calculations of equilibrium energies and physical properties, such as geometry and dipole moments, may be done using Hartree-Fock calculations.

Semiempirical calculations make assumptions beyond those used in the Hartree-Fock modeling. Possible effects due to electrons in filled quantum shells are ignored and further approximations are made. Nonetheless, semiempirical calculations are useful for determining heats of formation, equilibrium geometries of molecules, and geometries of transition states during reactions of molecules.

Other calculation methods include Møller-Plesset (MP2, MP3, etc.) and Density Functional (DFT) methods. DFT can be used much like Hartree-Fock, but the MP2 and MP3 methods require more calculation time.

Sample Calculation 5

Calculate the relative energies of the gauche and anti conformations of butane. How much more stable is the anti conformation than the eclipsed conformation having two eclipsed methyl groups? Compare calculations with the experimental values given in the lecture text and with the molecular mechanics values in Calculation 4.

Solution: After drawing the structure of butane, the program allows you to constrain the C2−C3 bond angle to 180° for the anti conformer. The calculated energy using SYBYL is 0.975 kcal/mol. Similarly, the energies for the 60° (gauche) and 0° (methyl-methyl eclipsed) conformers are 1.587 kcal/mol and 6.682 kcal/mol, respectively. Now setting the anti conformation to 0 kcal/mol and recalculating gives a gauche energy of 0.612 kcal/mol and methyl-methyl eclipsed energy of 5.707 kcal/mol. Compare these values with the values in Calculation 4.

Relative Energies of Butane Conformers

Conformation	Molecular mechanics (kcal/mol)	Hartree-Fock (kcal/mol)
Eclipsed	5.895	5.707
Gauche	0.617	0.612
Anti	0	0

For further practice repeat the calculations for propane and 2-methylbutane. Compare these results to those obtained in molecular mechanics Exercises Q.2 and Q.3.

Sample Calculation 6

Calculate the equilibrium geometry for formaldehyde, acetone, and benzaldehyde. Determine the dipole moment and net atomic charges on various atoms. Compare the relative order of the calculated dipole moments and compare with values reported in the CRC.

Solution: After drawing in the structures of each aldehyde or ketone, minimize the energy of each and calculate the charge on each atom and calculate the dipole moment of each compound using 3-21G* Hartree-Fock calculation. Calculated dipole moments compare favorably on a relative basis with experimental values.

Compound	Calculated dipole moment (D)	Experimental dipole moment (D)
Formaldehyde	2.64	2.3
Acetone	3.12	2.9
Benzaldehyde	3.38	3.0

The net charges on the carbonyl carbons are calculated to be 0.471 for formaldehyde, 0.830 for acetone, and 0.525 for benzaldehyde, whereas the carbonyl oxygens each have partial negative charges according to the calculations.

Using Molecular Mechanics with Quantum Mechanics

Calculations using quantum mechanics often start with a molecular geometry based upon a relatively fast molecular mechanics calculation. As a result, both approaches may be used for different parts of a calculation. For example, establishing the lowest-energy conformation required for a thermal rearrangement reaction, such as the Claisen rearrangement of allyl phenyl ether, can be done by first applying molecular mechanics to determine possible conformations of the molecule. The rearrangement calls for a chairlike transition state. Energies of the different possible conformations using AM1 geometries can be calculated. The energy of the most favorable chairlike conformation for reaction may be compared with the energy of the lowest energy conformation possible to calculate the energy required to get from the lowest energy conformation to the most favorable conformation for reaction. Applying molecular mechanics before AM1 facilitates the quantum mechanics calculation and shortens the overall calculation time.

allyl phenyl ether   transition state   2-allylphenol

Claisen rearrangement of allyl phenyl ether

Generally, when calculating relative energies and preferred conformations of a molecule such as 3-bromopropene in Sample Calculation 2, molecular mechanics MMFF and quantum mechanical Hartree-Fock and semiempirical AM1 and PM3 calculations are done at the same time (back-to-back). MMFF calculations are usually fast and Hartree-Fock calculations take longer, but otherwise modern software programs allow any and all of these calculations. To further pursue the relative energies of conformations of 3-bromopropene, let us calculate the preferred conformations of 3-bromopropene using both molecular mechanics and quantum mechanics calculations.

Sample Calculation 7

Calculate the dihedral angle of the preferred conformation of 3-bromopropene and the relative energy of the preferred conformation compared to the conformation having a dihedral angle of 0°.

Solution: From Calculation 2, the dihedral angle for C1−C2−C3−Br of the energy-minimized (preferred conformation) of 3-bromopropene using a molecular mechanics MMFF calculation is 118.34°. A summary of results from molecular mechanics and quantum mechanics calculations is shown here. (Note that 1 Hartree = 627.51 kcal/mol.)

Calculation method	Dihedral angle of preferred conformation	Energy of preferred conformation relative to the 0° conformation
MMFF	118.34°	−3.561 kcal/mol
AM1	111.18°	−1.414 kcal/mol
PM3	120.31°	−1.736 kcal/mol
Hartree-Fock 3.21G*	117.70°	−1.004 kcal/mol

Exercises involving quantum mechanics calculations for the determination of molecular properties such as equilibrium geometries, heats of formation and physical properties, charge densities in molecules, and other calculations may be found in the Critical Thinking sections of several experiments in this text, including Experiments 5.1, 6.1, 8.2, 12.2, 12.4 and other experiments.

Exercises

Part I Molecular Mechanics Exercises

Exercise Q.1: Conformational Analysis of Butane and Other Molecules

Calculate the relative energies for ten different conformations of butane (about the C2−C3 axis). Use the calculation software to plot energy (kcal/mol) vs dihedral angle. Alternatively, do calculations on a different molecule such as 1,2-dichloroethane, 1,2-dibromoethane, or another molecule assigned by the instructor.

Exercise Q.2: Conformational Analysis of Propane

Set the number of propane conformers desired using the calculation software and calculate the relative energies of the different conformers. Tabulate and compare with experimental data. Calculate the relative energies of propane conformers. Compare the calculated energies with the experimental values: eclipsed conformation, 2.90 kcal/mol; staggered conformation, 0 kcal/mol.

Exercise Q.3: Conformational Analysis of 2-Methylbutane

Calculate the relative energies of 2-methylbutane conformers. Compare the calculated energies with the predicted values based upon experiments: methyl-methyl eclipsed conformation, ~6.4 kcal/mol; hydrogen-methyl eclipsed conformations, 3.8 kcal/mol; dimethyl-methyl gauche conformation, 1.6 kcal/mol; methyl-methyl gauche conformation, 0.8 kcal/mol.

Part II Quantum Mechanics Exercises

Exercise Q.4: Identifying Reactive Sites

Determine the most reactive site for propanal and propanone with nucleophiles. This calculation can be done by determining the net charges. Reactive sites may also be visualized using orbital representations of electrostatic potential maps where relatively electron deficient regions are shown in blue and electron-rich regions are shown in red. For the lowest unoccupied molecular orbital (LUMO) of aldehydes and ketones, the electron density will show as a blue color over the carbonyl carbon and as a red color over the oxygen.

Exercise Q.5: Heats of Formation and Dipole Moments

Calculate the heats of formation and dipole moments for 1-butene, *cis*-2-butene, and *trans*-2-butene. Compare with the reported gas phase heats of formation (CRC, 2001, 5-25 to 5-60); 1-butene: 0.1 kcal/mol; *cis*-2-butene: −7.1 kcal/mol; *trans*-2-butene: −11.4 kcal/mol. Dipole moments are calculated for specific conformations. Compare the calculated values with experimental dipole moments (CRC, 2001, 9-44 to 9-50); 1-butene (cis): 0.438 Debyes (D); 1-butene (skew): 0.359 D; *cis*-2-butene: 0.253 D; *trans*-2-butene: 0 D.

Exercise Q.6: LUMO Energies of Alkenes

Compare the LUMO energies of the alkene π bonds of ethyl acrylate ($CH_2=CHCO_2CH_2CH_3$) and diethyl fumarate ($CH_3CH_2O_2CCH=CHCO_2CH_2CH_3$). The LUMO of lower energy (more negative value) generally reacts faster with electrons in the highest occupied molecular orbital of an electron pair donor molecule, such as in a Diels-Alder reaction (see Experiment 9.1). Use an AM1 calculation of initial geometry after selecting a Hartree-Fock single-point energy calculation. Which would be predicted to be more reactive, ethyl acrylate or diethyl fumarate?

Exercise Q.7: Conformational Analysis of 3-Fluoropropene

Use molecular mechanics MMFF and quantum mechanical Hartree-Fock and semi-empirical AM1 and PM3 calculations to calculate the preferred conformation of 3-fluoropropene. Compare the results with those obtained for 3-bromopropene. Do the calculations enable insight into molecular modeling by calculation vs using molecular models?

Reference

Lide, D. R., *CRC Handbook of Chemistry and Physics*, 82nd edition. CRC Press, Boca Raton, FL 2001.